TALK ABOUT CLASS! Here's a little 9-foot dory that weighs only 50 pounds and unfolds from a flat package. There's a slip-on rudder and pivoted leeboards that swing up out of the way for launching and beaching. Find out all about it on page 33. And check out all the other new sailboats starting on page 30

HERE IN FULL GLORY are the top 20 fishing lures from all over the world, as picked by our experts. These are the lures that are irresistible to the lunkers in both salt and fresh water. The article, on page 150, not only tells you *where* to fish, but also *how* to fish with them. For real fishing results, try these all-time winners!

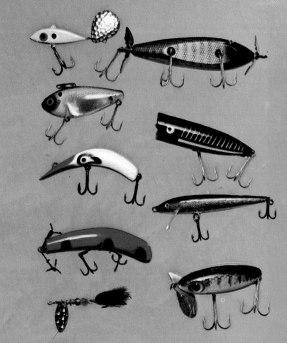

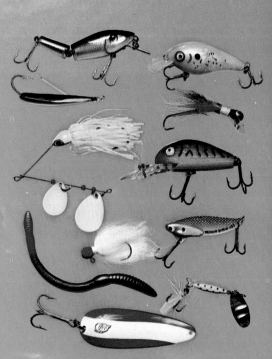

HERE ARE PATIO IDEAS GALORE! Use easy-to-build planters to provide bright splashes of color; gain extra seating—without extra furniture—by building handsome and comfortable steps; frame your patio with attractive railings. See the results below

MULTILEVEL DECK makes a prize-winning patio. Construction details start on page 78

DIVIDE AND CONQUER with a freestanding wall that enables two youngsters to share a single room. You needn't be a master carpenter, either! See the article on page 98

A STUNNING ADDITION to any home is this greenhouse packed with exotic blossoms. You assemble the structure from a kit. For details, plus plans for the potting benches, see page 4

SERVE YOUR GUESTS with a dash of elegance, then put down the tray and it becomes an attractive coffee table. The whole assembly is called a butler's table. See the plans on page 146

THIS EASY-TO-BUILD TRESTLE TABLE with matching benches may well become a family heirloom. Its beauty lies in the simplicity of its design and its hand-pegged construction. You'll find all the details on page 126

HERE'S A CHARMING CURIO SHELF that will show off your prize bric-a-brac with elegance, yet it's surprisingly easy to construct. It's a fine weekend project. Why not build it as a special, personal gift? For plans, see page 130

Popular Mechanics Do-It-Yourself Yearbook

1976

Exciting new products

- for your home
- for your shop
- 1976 cars
- gear for outdoorsmen
- the best of the new tools
- what's new for photographers
- newsmakers in electronics

Great projects of the year

- to improve your home
- shop know-how
- challenging craft projects
- how-to in the great outdoors
- photo projects
- electronics projects
- fun projects

Book Division, Hearst Magazines, New York, N.Y. 10019

EDITOR
Clifford B. Hicks

ART DIRECTOR
Ralph Leroy

ASSISTANT EDITORS
Donna Kalebic
Betty Meziere

ASSISTANT EDITOR, Production
Alfredo Vega

EDITORIAL ADVISORY BOARD, Popular Mechanics
John Linkletter, *Editor*
Sheldon Gallager, *Executive Editor*
Wayne C. Leckey, *Home and Shop Editor*
Daniel C. Fales, *Managing Editor*
Harry Wicks, *Home Workshop Editor*
William T. McKeown, *Outdoors Editor*
Ivan Berger, *Electronics and Photography Editor*

ISBN 0-910990-63-8

Library of Congress Catalog Number 75-23587

CONTENTS

This greenhouse for all seasons is available as a gable-roof freestanding unit as well as the lean-to shown in these photos

A greenhouse for your home!

BY ROBERT D. BORST

FOR YEARS, GARDENING and plant growing has been a seasonal hobby for our family. Until now, my wife's enthusiasm for growing things was exceeded only by her lack of it when each growing season ended. The greenhouse shown on these pages changed that.

Connected to the house proper, the lean-to structure is reached through a door installed in an opening in the concrete foundation. We selected the lean-to from a number of styles offered by the manufacturer, Lord & Burnham, Irvington-on-Hudson, N.Y. 10533. Called Orlyst pre-

Built from a kit, it adds charm to your home, and lets you enjoy the fun of gardening the year round. Here's how to build and equip one for your house

The first step is to open all packages, removing and sorting all parts into like piles.
The parts are then checked against the packing lists to make sure all parts are on hand.
Next, the blueprints should be carefully studied so the assembly is understood

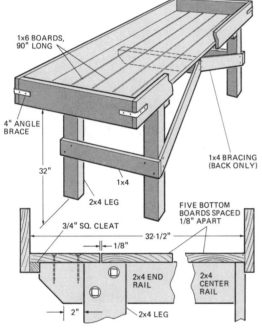

1x6 BOARDS, 90" LONG

4" ANGLE BRACE

1x4 BRACING (BACK ONLY)

32"

1x4

2x4 LEG

3/4" SQ. CLEAT

FIVE BOTTOM BOARDS SPACED 1/8" APART

32-1/2"

1/8"

2x4 END RAIL

2x4 CENTER RAIL

2"

2x4 LEG

build a greenhouse, continued

After the house shingles are removed, ⅜-in. shims are nailed to the house sheathing

A 2x8 header is installed using lagscrews. The deck bars of the greenhouse attach to the header

Concrete-footing forms are used; spreaders keep batter boards from toeing-in during the pour

Anchors hold greenhouse sills in place on the concrete. This installation must be accurate

fabricated greenhouses, their prices range from about $500 to $2500 (cost varies with the number of sections used). The six-section, 16-foot-long structure shown costs around $1500 delivered.

The greenhouse kit arrives in several packages, so the first step is to unpack the parts and sort them into like piles for checking. Complete as-

The door frame is positioned; the concrete footing must be 1 to 2 in. above the grade

The greenhouse frame is braced in position; 1x2 spacers are then installed

The deck frame is fastened to the 2x8 header on the house by means of wood screws

The ridge and 2x4 stringer for the deck are attached. The operable vent is below

Vertical 2x4s are used temporarily to support the deck stringer during the frame assembly

The vent shaft is positioned and installed after the main members are fastened in place

Tongue-and-groove sheathing is fastened to the deck. It is then trimmed in place

The operable vent sash is the next to be installed. It aids in temperature control

The closure channel is attached to the doorbars and the door is hung in the gable end

sembly instructions come with the kit. They should be read and understood before you start building.

The "hard work" part of the job is the digging, forming and pouring of the footings. To ease the pouring task somewhat, we used transit (ready-mix) concrete wheelbarrowed from truck to forms. At the forms, the concrete was pushed into job-built "pour boxes" to speed placement in the footing forms (see photos, page 8). Since the glass is precut for an exact fit, the footings are poured *after* the structure is erected and glazed. Done this way, the structure will be absolutely square and the glass panels will slide into place effortlessly.

Our house is on sloping terrain. Thus, the

A gauge determines the precise location of the eave. Glazing locks the structure square

The vent-section glass goes on first, followed by the panes on the roof, side and gables

Glass panels are bedded in a foam tape. The joints are sealed with a top compound

A bar cap is installed next, with sheet-metal screws serving to keep the glass in place

Concrete footings are poured after the frame is up, and glazed, to assure the glass will fit

The concrete was pushed into the trench through an 8-in.-wide opening in the bottom

The 17,000 B.T.U. electric unit-heater under the potting bench is thermostat-operated

This humidifier, with humidistat, from Lord & Burnham, sells for about $100

The vent motor, small and quiet, opens and closes the vent section automatically

greenhouse could be attached to the basement wall and permit a direct entrance from the basement. Here, it was a must to cut an opening for the door before the green house was glazed.

utilities you'll need

Obviously, water is first. You'll be wise to install an ample number of hose bibs for conven-

ience. A tub for cleanup and pot-washing is also helpful.

You will want electricity for the operation of basic equipment, and grounded outlets. For safety, *every piece* of electrical equipment should be grounded in accordance with the National Electrical Code. Be sure to provide for utilities before pouring footings.

Rubber-jointed ceramic tile

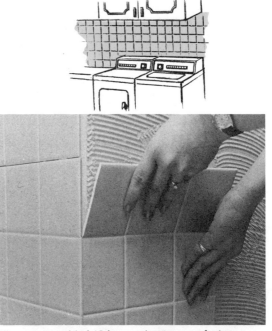

Six colors of tile are available. Five 12x12-in. 9-tile sheets total about $9.50; eight tub-surround sheets of 49 tiles each, plus cove, sell for around $100

The preassembled 12-in.-sq. sheets go on fast. Joint spacing has already been set; you simply press the sheets firmly in the adhesive

■ DO-IT-YOURSELFERS can now buy genuine ceramic tile in pregrouted sheets. American Olean Tile Co., Lansdale, Pa. 19446, is now offering two basic systems, both called Easy-Set, in which the tiles come mounted in sheets and joints are prefilled with a silicone rubber that stays permanently flexible. One system consists of 12x12-in. sheets of nine tiles each for walls, vanity tops, back-splashes and shower and tub surrounds. The second comprises a packaged tub surround of eight large sheets of 49 tiles each, plus cove.

With the tiles preassembled in easy-to-handle sheets, the tiling goes fast with less mess. The sheets are cemented to the wall with a water-resistant mastic. Butting joints are filled with Dow Corning 734 sealant applied with a caulking gun. Joints are smoothed and excess sealant is removed with cheesecloth and denatured alcohol. Tile cutters are available for custom-fitting the tiles to existing appliances. The pregrouted sheets are available in six different colors.

Facelifts for your home

More and more new products for home exteriors are appearing on the market. Here are seven of the many types which can beautify your home

■ EACH SPRING, millions of Americans emerge from winter hibernation—ladder and paint bucket in hand—to start the annual assault on the exteriors of their homes. Most are justifiably concerned about how the house looks, because it's the exterior that is constantly on display.

The latest, and growing, trend in fixing up the house has been to cover unsightly siding and start afresh. Building-product manufacturers are aware of this. Thus a larger-than-ever selection of siding materials is now available. See the article on page 89, "Re-siding: you can do it yourself," for more information on how to proceed.

There are six basic exterior sidings available to the homeowner: aluminum, asbestos, insulated (similar to roof shingles), steel, vinyl and wood. On these pages several types are shown. Before making a final decision you should visit your local lumberyard to determine if yet another type of siding suits your home, taste and budget better. Questions you should ask about a siding are: How do weather, pollution and dirt affect it? Does it offer good insulation and termite protection?

Ideal for re-siding and new construction, vinyl clapboard (above) is made by Certain-Teed Products Corp. If you prefer wood, consider one of U.S. Plywood's prestained textured sidings (Oldbridge, right). They're available in many different sizes including 4x8, 4x9 and 4x10, and in 26 different colors

Material to suit every taste: 1. Redwood plywood, inverted batten pattern; 2. Stuccato siding, Masonite Corp.; 3. 4x8-ft. textured hardboard, Georgia-Pacific Corp.; 4. shingle-siding (16x48-in. size), Boise Cascade; 5. vinyl soffit and fascia, Bird & Son

Water by the pushbutton

BY WAYNE C. LECKEY

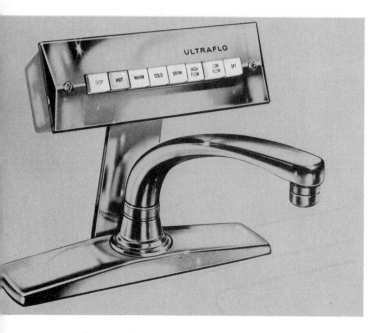

| DISP | HOT | WARM | COLD | DRINK | HI FLO | LO FLO | OFF |

There are eight buttons for the kitchen sink. When OFF button is pushed, the only water left in the line is in the 3-ft. section between water tank and valve unit

Turning a faucet is a thing of the past with a new plumbing system called Ultraflo. You start the water flowing by merely pressing a button

■ YOU CAN NOW TURN ON a faucet by pressing a button. It's all made possible by a console containing banks of solenoid valves located near the water heater. The banks are electrically operated (12 volts) by pushbutton control panels located at your kitchen sink, bathtub and lavatory. There are eight button selections for the kitchen sink marked: DISPOSER, HOT, WARM, COLD, DRINK, HI FLO, LO FLO and OFF. At each lavatory and bathtub there are four button selections. If you want hot water, you press the HOT button and in seconds you have water of a preselected temperature. No longer is it necessary to let the water run to "hurry" it (hot or cold) to the faucet—it's there as soon as you press the button.

Not only does this unique system eliminate the need to replace faucet washers and help save water and the cost of heating it, but the system costs less to install since it replaces the conventional two-pipe (hot and cold) system with only a single line. Flexible copper or plastic tubing no larger than ¼- or ⅜-in. is all that's needed to supply each fixture because you no longer have to manually mix hot and cold water as with a conventional system. It's done for you at a water-mixing source.

At the time of installation, the rate of flow and temperature of the water is preset. Temperature range is from 102° to 114°F.–102°F. is luke-warm; 114°F. is as hot as one can stand. For

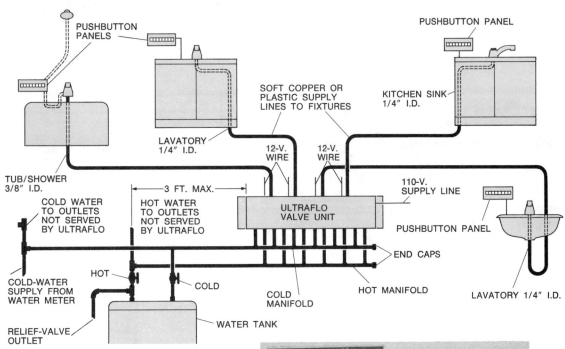

PUSHBUTTON PANELS

PUSHBUTTON PANEL

SOFT COPPER OR PLASTIC SUPPLY LINES TO FIXTURES

KITCHEN SINK 1/4" I.D.

LAVATORY 1/4" I.D.

TUB/SHOWER 3/8" I.D.

12-V. WIRE

12-V. WIRE

110-V. SUPPLY LINE

3 FT. MAX.

COLD WATER TO OUTLETS NOT SERVED BY ULTRAFLO

HOT WATER TO OUTLETS NOT SERVED BY ULTRAFLO

ULTRAFLO VALVE UNIT

PUSHBUTTON PANEL

END CAPS

COLD-WATER SUPPLY FROM WATER METER

HOT

COLD

COLD MANIFOLD

HOT MANIFOLD

LAVATORY 1/4" I.D.

RELIEF-VALVE OUTLET

WATER TANK

How Ultraflo works

KITCHEN SWITCH	BUTTON PROVIDES
HOT	Water directly from the hot-water supply.
WARM	Hot and cold water blended to preset temperature desired by the user.
COLD	Water directly from the cold-water supply.
DRINK	Water directly from the cold-water supply bypassing the water softener (when applicable) to provide more palatable drinking water.
DISPOSER	Simultaneous operation of disposal unit and cold-water flow.
HIGH FLOW	Maximum preset water flow desired by user.
LOW FLOW	Reduced water flow when desired.
OFF	Shutoff of all activity generated by the switch.

LAVATORY SWITCH	BUTTON PROVIDES
HOT	Water directly from the hot-water supply.
WARM	Water blended to preset temperature desired by the user.
COLD	Water directly from the cold-water supply.
OFF	Shutoff of all flow of water to the fixture.

SHOWER/TUB SWITCH	BUTTON PROVIDES
WARM	Water blended to preset temperature desired by the user.
WARM 2	Water blended to greater temperature than the WARM setting.
WARM 3	Water blended to higher temperature than the WARM 2 setting.
OFF	Shutoff of all flow of water to the fixture.

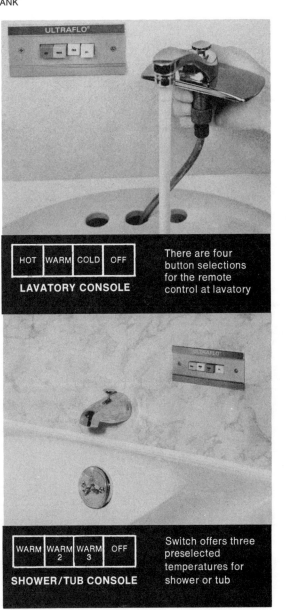

| HOT | WARM | COLD | OFF |

LAVATORY CONSOLE

There are four button selections for the remote control at lavatory

| WARM | WARM 2 | WARM 3 | OFF |

SHOWER/TUB CONSOLE

Switch offers three preselected temperatures for shower or tub

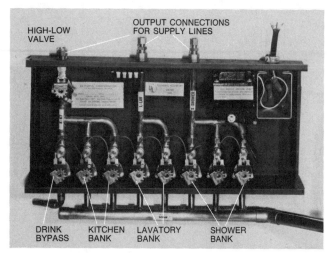

A valve unit, near the hot-water tank, contains solenoids to control temperature and flow

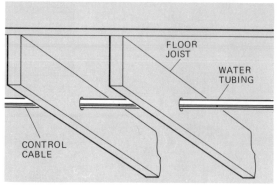

Both the single water line and the wiring run from switch to valve through the joists

push-button water supply, continued

bathing and showering, the temperature is preset at 106° to 108°F. Presetting the flow and temperature settings of the solenoid valves requires the flat blade of a screwdriver. Once set, the valves normally do not require readjustment.

For more information about this unique, one-line pushbutton plumbing, write to the Ultraflo Corp., Box 2284, Sandusky, Ohio 44870.

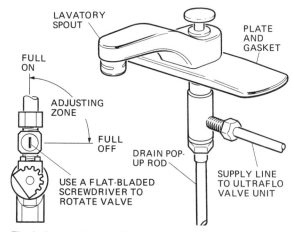

The balance valves (left) restrict flow and regulate the temperature. They are preset initially with a screwdriver

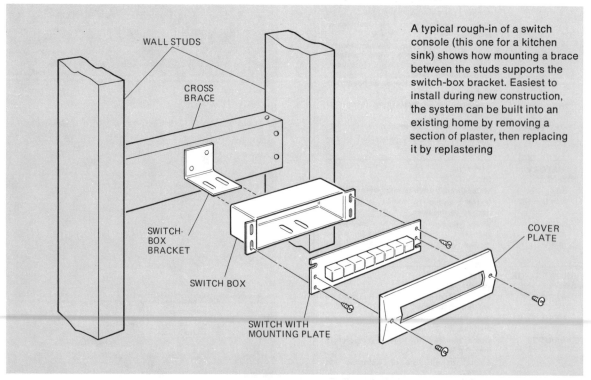

A typical rough-in of a switch console (this one for a kitchen sink) shows how mounting a brace between the studs supports the switch-box bracket. Easiest to install during new construction, the system can be built into an existing home by removing a section of plaster, then replacing it by replastering

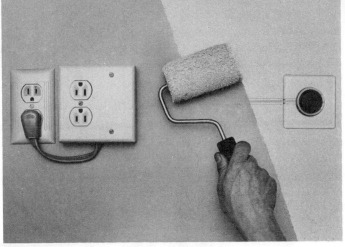

The mounted-on-the-wall switch system consists of an adhesive-backed, plug-in transformer (power unit) placed next to an existing duplex receptacle (above left), sticky-back, two-wire conductor tape and a switch. The wire is hidden with wallpaper or two coats of paint

Quick-install surface switch

You can install a wall switch near any existing receptacle in just 30 minutes with this new child-safe low-voltage system. Everything sticks right to the wall

A second type of power unit, also used with conductor tape and a touchbutton switch, is mounted inside a standard octagonal ceiling outlet, or a double-gang receptacle as at bottom. When installed, the power unit steps down house circuit to a child-safe 2 volts

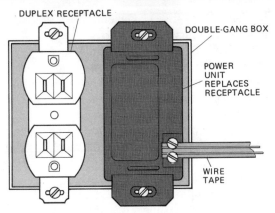

DUPLEX RECEPTACLE

DOUBLE-GANG BOX

POWER UNIT REPLACES RECEPTACLE

WIRE TAPE

■ INSTALLING A NEW wall switch used to mean cutting a hole in the wall for the switchbox and one or more holes for the tedious job of snaking the wires inside the wall from the fixture or outlet to the desired switch location. Then came the nuisance of patching before you could paint. Now, everything from lamps and TVs to stereos and airconditioners can be controlled by a wall switch so easy to install that a housewife or home-owner with little or no electrical knowledge can do it.

Called "Surface Switch," this UL-approved system has three adhesive-backed components that are simply pressed against the wall: a plug-in, solid-state relay transformer (power unit) placed next to an existing single-gang receptacle, 15 feet of .005-in.-thick two-wire conductor tape and a clear plastic, wafer-thin touchbutton switch. The power unit steps down 110-120v. power to a 2-v. level, claimed to be so safe that if a child cut into the wire, the extremely low voltage would not be felt.

An alternate design, using the conductor tape and switch as before, has a separate power unit installed inside a double-gang wall receptacle or ceiling fixture outlet as shown at left. It's made by Switchpack Systems, Inc., 11578 Sorrento Valley Rd., San Diego, Calif. 92121. Plug-in unit kit, about $15; separate power-unit kit, about $13; available in hardware and department stores. Extra touchbuttons can be bought for multiple switching.

Mercury vapor lamp uses less energy

BY ROBERT W. TUREK

You can install a new post lamp or convert an existing light and take advantage of this energy-saver. Mercury vapor bulbs burn brighter and longer than incandescent

■ TODAY, ELECTRIC POST LAMPS offer the most economical and protective illumination for your driveway, walk, steps and entrances. Thanks to a new mercury vapor bulb, you can now illuminate the outside of your home with a brighter, longer-lasting light that uses less energy.

Compared to a typical 100-w. household-type bulb, a 50-w. mercury vapor bulb lasts 21 times as long and gives off almost twice as much light per watt. A 100-w. household bulb lasts about 750 hours (three months if lighted an average of eight hours a day), but the mercury bulb will burn about 16,000 hours (more than five years at the same daily rate). General Electric is one maker of mercury vapor bulbs.

The new elliptical mercury bulb operates on a 120-v. circuit. But since it requires a ballast, it cannot simply be screwed into a conventional light socket. Several outdoor lighting manufacturers, including Hacco, McGraw-Edison, Artolier and Montgomery Ward, have designed cast-aluminum postlight fixtures for the mercury vapor bulb. They offer excellent light distribution from an unbreakable lens.

Before installing a new lamp, check with your local building department to assure electrical code

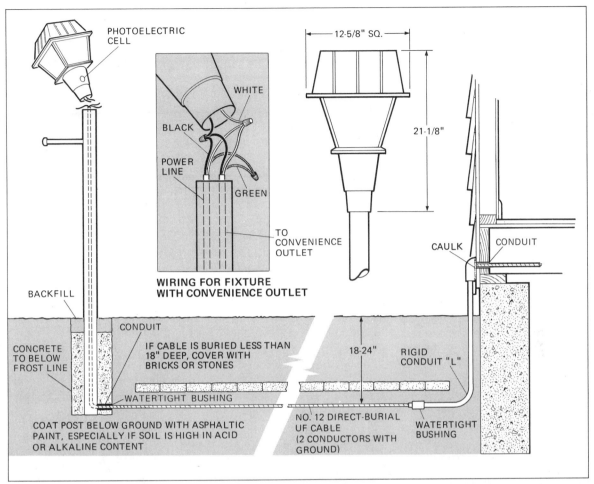

PHOTOELECTRIC CELL

12-5/8" SQ.

21-1/8"

WHITE

BLACK

POWER LINE

GREEN

TO CONVENIENCE OUTLET

WIRING FOR FIXTURE WITH CONVENIENCE OUTLET

CAULK

CONDUIT

BACKFILL

CONDUIT

IF CABLE IS BURIED LESS THAN 18" DEEP, COVER WITH BRICKS OR STONES

18-24"

RIGID CONDUIT "L"

CONCRETE TO BELOW FROST LINE

WATERTIGHT BUSHING

COAT POST BELOW GROUND WITH ASPHALTIC PAINT, ESPECIALLY IF SOIL IS HIGH IN ACID OR ALKALINE CONTENT

NO. 12 DIRECT-BURIAL UF CABLE (2 CONDUCTORS WITH GROUND)

WATERTIGHT BUSHING

Converting a standard electric post light can be as simple as removing the existing fixture head, and reconnecting the mercury vapor lamp

compliance. Then dig a post hole—lower than the area frost line—and a trench to the power source, following details in the diagram above. Once the cable is laid in the trench and wired through the post, place the post in the hole, plumb and secure it in both planes with rope and stakes (see page 18). Usually a 45-lb. bag of concrete mix will fill the hole to about 6 in. below ground level. Backfill the hole and trench, and replace sod. Pull a plastic bag over the post top and seal it with tape to guard against moisture. Let concrete set 24 to 48 hours, then remove bag and mount the fixture head by wiring as follows:

mercury vapor lamps, continued

To wire fixture only. Attach the black cable wire to the black fixture wire, white cable wire to the white fixture wire, and green wire to ground on cable.

To wire the outdoor, weatherproof convenience outlet to provide a plug-in receptacle at the post. Connect the black convenience-outlet (CO) wire to the black cable wire, white CO wire to white cable wire and green CO wire to ground wire on the cable.

To wire a photoelectric-cell collar to the fixture. (This device turns light on at dusk, off at dawn.) Connect the white wire from the photo cell and fixture to the white cable wire; connect the black wire from the photo cell to the black cable wire; then connect the red wire from the photo cell to the black fixture wire. Aim photo cell toward the north.

To wire a photoelectric cell, convenience outlet and fixture. Connect the white wires from the fixture, photo cell and convenience outlet (CO) to white cable wire; connect the black fixture wire to the red wire on the photo cell; connect the black wires from the photo cell and CO to black cable wire; then connect the green CO wire to ground wire on the cable. Use solderless connectors and wrap with electrical tape.

If the power source is a surface outlet on the exterior of your house, turn off the circuit and attach an L-shaped conduit to the outlet box. Pull cable wire through the conduit and connect it to corresponding color-coded wires in the outlet—white to white, black to black. If an outside outlet is not available, run conduit through the basement wall and make connections at the nearest junction box (see diagram, page 17).

A metal fixture or post must be grounded. When no convenience outlet is used, run ground wire to fixture. With an outlet (which can also be wired at base of the post), ground the receptacle box to the ground post and fixture. A waterproof outlet box at the house entry should have an internal ground screw for ground-wire connection.

Converting a gas post light is easy, but the gas line should be capped by a professional gas-pipe installer.

INSTALLATION OF LAMP POST

INSTALLATION TOOLS AND MATERIALS

MATERIALS

1. No. 12 direct-burial type UF cable wire (2 conductors with ground)
2. Solderless connectors (6)
3. Plastic electrical tape
4. 45-lb. bag of dry concrete mix
5. Heavy-plastic bag (minimum 4-in. dia.)
6. Rope
7. Stakes (4)
8. L-shaped conduit
9. Conduit sleeves (2)
10. Watertight bushings (2)

TOOLS

1. Spade
2. Long-nose pliers
3. Wire stripper
4. Screwdriver

KEEP POST PLUMB WITH ROPE AND STAKES WHILE CONCRETE SETS

PLUMB POST IN BOTH PLANES

POSTHOLE, 18-24" DEEP, 8" DIA.

TRENCH 18-24" DEEP FOR DIRECT BURIAL CABLE

Informality and English Tudor styling are the keynotes of this playroom. Styling is created by using textured surfaces on the walls and ceiling

Prefinished indoor-outdoor siding made to resemble stucco was used to give this family playroom an English Tudor feeling. The ceiling is also covered with textured hardboard and finished with false beams

'Stucco' your walls by the sheet

■ AN L-SHAPED BASEMENT with an area of 900 sq. ft. is the spacious setting for a dual-purpose family room built by a couple for their family of six. In the area most used by the adults, a wet bar and a bumper-pool table were installed. The basic entertainment feature in the area set aside for the youngsters of the household is a table-tennis outfit.

Informality was the watchword in planning this playroom. To achieve it, the walls were covered with Stuccato indoor-outdoor siding which is made to resemble stucco. The ceiling, set with floodlights to provide illumination where it is needed, was covered with a prefinished, textured hardboard called Surfstone. Both the textured wall and ceiling panels are manufactured by Masonite Corp. and priced at about $15 per panel. The panels are supplied in standard 4 ft. x 8 ft. size. False beams and half-timbers were used to enhance the English Tudor styling. These were made from strips of an umber-stained, rough-sawn hardboard siding cut to the proper size.

This close-up photo shows Stuccato's texture. This paneling was used on the walls

The ceilings are covered with Surfstone. The "beams" are stained strips of hardboard

New for the homeowner

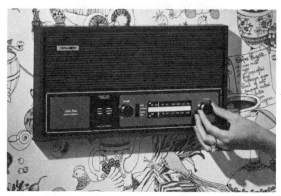

NUTONE'S LATEST in-a-wall AM/FM radio intercom includes a burglar-alarm system that uses entry detector switches on doors and windows. If an intruder attempts entry, an alarm sounds indoors and through an outside speaker. The alarm also sounds if the system is accidentally turned off. For prices, write NuTone, Madison and Red Bank Rds., Cincinnati, Ohio 45227

FOR THOSE who haven't settled permanently, the Maytag dishwasher (below) offers portability with permanent installation possible later by means of a conversion kit. The new model has casters and is hooked to a sink faucet for its water source. It's available in 4 colors. Maytag, Newton, Iowa 50208

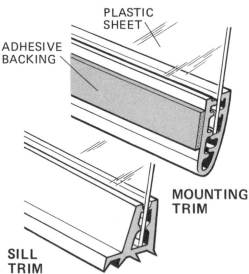

PLASTIC SHEET

ADHESIVE BACKING

MOUNTING TRIM

SILL TRIM

MEET THE IN-SIDER, a new interior storm window designed to stop drafts on windows without outside storms. No ladder to climb, you apply it directly to the window frame from inside the room. No special tools are needed—you just measure, cut and press in place. A rigid crystal-olear sheet of 1/16-in. plastic fits tightly into strips of adhesive-backed, vinyl mounting trim. To remove the storm, you simply unsnap the lip of the trim and lift out the pane. The white trim, which you can paint, remains attached to casing and sill. In four stock sizes, it's a product of Plaskolite, Inc., 1770 Joyce Ave., Columbus, Ohio 43219

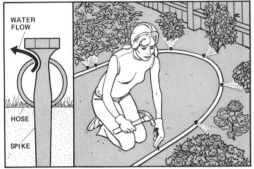

WATER
FLOW

HOSE

SPIKE

YOU CAN CREATE your own watering system with Sprinkler Spikes and an inexpensive garden hose. The spikes are hammered through the hose into the ground (above); slotted spike heads control the amount of water released. A package of six spikes is about $2 from The Simpler Co., Box 868, Saratoga, Calif. 95070

AN INTERIOR DOORWAY can add to storage space with this door and a built-in, 7½-inch-deep cabinet (above). The supporting door is made of 1⅜-inch solid pine with reinforcing aluminum frame. The price is about $130 without hardware from Space Analysts, Inc., 2247 East 16 St., Brooklyn, N.Y. 11229

HIDE-A-PIPE VANITIQUE not only conceals an unsightly lavatory trap but provides extra storage space for supplies. The molded styrene unit comes in pink, yellow, blue, black or white, measures 16 by 18 by 20 in., fits under most 17 by 19-in. and larger lavatories and installs with six screws. About $35 from Hide-A-Pipe Co., 510 South Ave. W., Westfield, New Jersey 07090

Pivot point for car manufacturers

Last year—1975—was the year that turned Detroit
upside-down; 1976 is likely to be the year that
will turn it rightside up again and point it toward
small cars with built-in fuel economy,
environmental safeguards—and personal safety

BY ED NELSON

■ THOSE WHO FOLLOW the fortunes of the auto world are unlikely to call Detroit a revolutionary hotbed.

But revolution has come to our cars—at least in Detroit's cautious context. Some call it a revolution of good sense. Sparks first appeared during the 1975 model run, then increased with the '76s. Why? Proliferating standards for safer cars using less resources and doing less damage to our environment are major stimuli. So is the ailing world economy.

The plainest sign of the coming revolution was in cars' changing size. Early in 1975, for the first time, a compact (Chevrolet's Nova) took the lead in new-car registrations. And Vega took second. In mid-year, American Motors introduced its Pacer, a genuinely new small car that drew grudging salute even from competitors' styling and design chiefs. It made headlines: "Pacer . . . cuts into all markets."

a small Caddy

Cadillac then introduced what spokesmen had said would never see daylight: a small Caddy. The new Seville 4-door bowed with a 350-CID, fuel-injected V-8. Its over-all length and wheelbase are a touch shorter than the Chevelle's and the Seville is over 5 inches narrower than the Pacer. But the august Cadillac Motor Car Division guarded itself from any hint it was building cut-rate products: Seville's introductory price tag read $12,479, soon to pass $13 thousand.

As change accelerated, Chrysler's proud Imperial couldn't cut the mustard. Chrysler dropped the Imperial from its 1976 menu.

Alone in Detroit, Chrysler couldn't come up with a new American small car.

Chrysler looked for something—almost anything—to spark buyers. It offered a "new size"

compact, the Volare, from Chrysler-Plymouth for '76 (as a Dodge, it is the Aspen). Under either name, the size is less startling than suggested. There are two sizes, actually. Two-door coupes are on a 108.5-inch wheelbase; the 4-doors on 112.5. So the Aspen/Volare frame is ½ to 1½ inches longer than the '76 Dart/Valiant's. A "new size"?

Truly new to the U.S. is Chevy's international Chevette. That had been its name in Brazil. Then it was built in Germany as an Opel Kadette, in Britain as a Vauxhall Chevette, in Japan as an Isuzu Gemini, and in Australia as a Holden Gemini. A 2-door hatchback on a 94.3-inch wheelbase, it's driven by an 85-CID, overhead-cam Four. The engine is 59 pounds lighter than Vega's, the over-all length 16 inches shorter.

As 1976 began, five-speed transmissions spread quickly. Monza announced the availability first as '75 models faded. Production trouble delayed real installation, but the new box was announced for Monza's '76 siblings in other GM divisions.

Even Ford, with little major news for '76, illustrated Detroit's good-sense small-car mood. The little Pinto showed up with a painted grille, fully as attractive as familiar chromed die-castings, but easier and cheaper to repair as needed.

Ford couldn't respond immediately to the Chevette, but its new Bobcat was due, probably during '76. Not the reworked Pinto that Lincoln-Mercury named Bobcat, but the European Bobcat that Ford was building in Spain. Not to be outdone, Volvo was reported testing the little Daf in the States.

battle over air bags

Government standards for safer cars kept coming, with the boiling battle over passive restraints making the most news. The principal passive system uses air bags that deploy automatically to cushion occupants in a crash.

John Z. DeLorean brought impressive credentials to the air-bag fight. A sharp young GM vice-president, he first got public attention as Pontiac general manager. He moved up the corporate ladder despite his tendency to speak out on industry responsibility, a personal interest in exotic foreign cars, and his resistance to the classic GM mold. DeLorean finally resigned in 1973. But he kept speaking out.

He shrugged off the much-talked-of problem of fitting bags into small cars. It was plainly, he said, "capable of solution." Asking delay on passive restraints, Detroit stressed needed lead time. DeLorean said companies always raised a certain amount of "fuss and feathers," but installation generally "could be done on a routine basis."

GM offered air-bag options on 1975 big cars, but not the 4341-pound 1975½ Seville. The company said it didn't know a way to fit them into smaller cars, although Volvo got them into 75 3000-pound sedans.

Fuel economy was crucial as gas prices marched up amid a chorus of charges and counter-charges. Oil companies, Middle Eastern nations, bad driving habits, politicians, and gas-hungry cars all were blamed.

Car builders blamed government, saying standards for less vulnerability to fender-benders dictated heavier bumpers, and that the weight gobbled gas. Consumer groups charged Detroit took the easy way out with heavy bumpers, then passed the buck.

Parts of government, in turn, aimed at car builders as the culprits. The Federal Trade Commission began seeking ways to compel meaningful, understandable, legitimately comparable economy claims.

misleading tests?

Fuel-thrifty cars were hard to identify as one set of tests was cited here, another there. Self-styled experts assailed EPA data as misleading, inaccurate, or incomplete. Few bothered to note that varied procedures had to give varied results.

EPA tests, on a chassis dynamometer, treat each car identically. The time and amount of acceleration, braking, even ambient temperature are controlled. The agency warns that individuals' results will vary from the EPA numbers, but insists its data compare competing cars in realistic circumstances. Options going on a third of a particular model, for example, must be on the car

EPA tests. Results spurred smaller U.S. cars when the first list of 244 '75 cars had *no* U.S. models in the VW-dominated top 10, only two in the top 20.

Environmental hornets gave Detroit more bad dreams. U.S. builders leaned more heavily on catalytic converters to control emissions, but John Moran, an EPA scientist, said converters themselves emitted threatening sulfates. Moran's report was countered in a few weeks by one from another EPA scientist, but the agency had already set back a long-delayed stiffer standard. Then emission controls manufacturers released yet a third report, this by two former EPA scientists, attacking Moran's work.

Other officials charged the converters could be grass- or forest-fire causes.

Impending 1977 emission standards were blamed for another delay in the long-awaited GM rotary engine. The Pacer, planned for GM's rotary, got AMC's 232-CID Six. But the latest delay might be brief; rumors flew in Detroit that GM had slashed the Wankel hydrocarbon emissions dramatically.

Continuing auto tumult reached even omnipresent Volkswagenwerk. After 16 years atop the U.S. import market, VW was passed by both Toyota and Datsun. An American-built Volks just might result. The dollar's waning value meant U.S. money paid for VWs was worth less in Germany. VW's new young president visited Chrysler seeking some co-op set-up by which VWs could be built—or at least assembled—in the States. But he faced obstacles at home. Two-thirds of VW's Supervisory Board must okay moving German auto workers' jobs to the U.S. And 14 of its 21 members are workers themselves or are from labor-oriented political units.

foreign companies struggling

Other foreign-car companies faced fiscal punishment in 1976, some struggling to stay afloat. Chances for a Citroen-Peugot merger faded as Citroen began losing money. In Great Britain, British Leyland stockholders okayed a plan for government to take over and run their firm. And Italy's hallowed GT firm, Maserati, was on the block again.

Crystal balls are always cloudy, but there was little doubt the revolution was slowly closing the door on the big cars that have exemplified America. Robert Lienert, editor of a respected trade journal, said the standard-size U.S. car was on its death-bed. The car of the future, he said, will be small, light, with more glass, and probably Wankel-powered.

Sew your own camp gear

BY BILL MCKEOWN

Several hours of easy work can cut your costs in half and at the same time assure you of quality equipment which will last through many camping trips

Sew-it-yourself Aspen jacket comes in kit from Frostline for about $26. A few hours' work converts pieces into quality down-filled coat valued at almost $50

■ HOW WOULD YOU like a 50-percent discount on camping gear that you need? Not cheap equipment, either, but the very best obtainable—finely made and probably better than any you could order anywhere.

Nor is your choice limited to a handwoven belt or watch band. Look over the list below and see if there isn't an item—or, more likely, many—that you wish you had:

Down-filled sleeping bag
Bag liner
Bivouac cover
Down jacket
Parka
Ski coat
Down vest
Down sweater
Down pants
Gaiters
Poncho
Booties
Overboots
Chaps
Rain gear
Tent
Stuff sack and backpack
Bike bag

Many of these come in assorted sizes, types and colors, while the variety of items offered is growing all the time.

At first glance, a price tag of $100 for a sleeping-bag kit or tent kit can seem steep, especially since you still have to put it together. But if you don't enjoy working with your hands, you probably wouldn't take up camping, and the kit manufacturers have found their customers already know about but don't want the flimsy cut-rate items from some surplus outlets. For example, if you buy a sleeping-bag kit for about $84 which is rated for −20° F. and then add the optional $21 worth of "expedition down fill" for even more insulation, it's obvious you want the best. Or perhaps you select a model which weighs about five and a half pounds for about $60. You can sew the special full-length foam pad right into the down bag, where it is always ready for use.

Because you or your wife do the sewing, you can be sure that no one took shortcuts on inside seams that don't show, and you can also double stitch or lock stitch spots where you know from experience a zipper can tear or a D-ring pull loose when you're miles from nowhere. Basic sewing experience is helpful, though not essential, and these kits could be sewn by hand rather than machine if you had a lot of time. According to a spokesman for the EMSkit division of Eastern Mountain Sports, "Novices seem to understand the instructions more easily than experienced seamstresses, and the most satisfied customers are those who enjoy making their own equipment rather than those who try to save money." And any man who thinks that only women can sew has never been a bachelor very long, or hasn't visited a sail loft recently.

To test kit instructions and materials, and because they looked great, we first selected down booties, about $6, and overboots, about $5, avail-

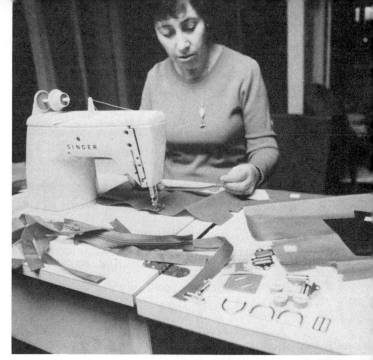

able in blue, green, or orange. Both came with all the materials—thread, elastic, cord and laces—plus illustrated instructions so explicit that some-one who had never sewn before could have worked them out.

Even after years of sewing, Virginia Hricko had never edge-seared fabric, but the instructions made it easy. You carefully pass a flame along the edge of the Ripstop Nylon without touching it. The heat seals the edge so that it will never unravel during wear, washing, or cleaning. It is easy to see why in normal factory assembly there's not time to spare for refinements such as this.

Many of the products come in a variety of sizes, ranging down to clothing for children and pack carriers for babies. Some of the sleeping bags start with 42-inch lengths, and then can later be extended with 12-inch sections as the youngster grows. Provided in small plastic packs is the down you will use to fill the insulated cloth-ing and bags. This, we found, is a neat and easy way to handle the very fluffy feathers.

And even if you have no plans for camping or cool-weather sports, the kit makers' catalogs deserve study for their versatile bargain travel packs and bags. We test-constructed kits from each, and found them uniformly well designed. They were complete with all necessary parts, and with instructions that told both the how, and reassuringly, the why of each succeeding step.

Cross-country and downhill skiers, hunters, bicyclists and travelers using almost any other means of getting around are likely to find kits designed especially for them.

Though it would be hard to select our favorite kit to sew up and use, our best bag-title award would certainly go to Eastern Mountain Sports for their $16 model in navy or orange. It's the EMSkit Knapsack-snackpack Rucksack. It proved to be easier to sew than to say.

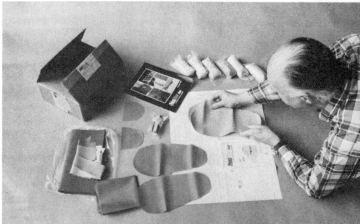

Turning parts into a pack took an evening, Virginia Hricko (top) found, after following kit's complete instructions and using all the comprehensive enclosures. Fabrics, goosedown packs and thread were in the boot and bootie kits (center). Final reward of a needlework (below) is a bargain in quality gear

Kit manufacturers

CARIKITS
Holubar, Box 7, Boulder, Colo. 80302.

EMSKITS
Eastern Mountain Sports, Inc., 1041 Common-wealth Ave., Boston, Mass. 02215.

FROSTLINE
Frostline Kits, 452 Burbank, Broomfield, Colo. 80020.

MAKIT
Mountain Adventure Kits, Box 571, Whittier, Calif. 90608.

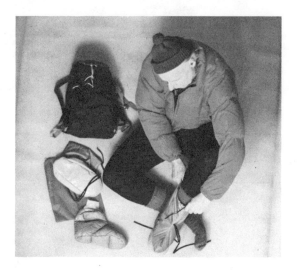

Canoes that take less paddle power

More white-water action,
or quiet, leisurely boating with
minimum arm energy, are among
the advantages offered by new
designs and the latest materials

BY JEROME KNAP

Modern models are designed to handle rougher
water, tip less easily, float if swamped or
capsized. Foam pontoons (top) from Grumman
Boats can be added for increased stability.
Sawyer's Cruiser (above) offers both racing
and cruising ability in a 17-foot 9-inch
fiberglass hull that weighs only 68 pounds

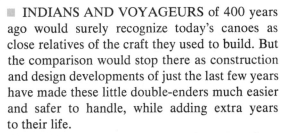

Rushton (above) from Old Town Canoes, is 18-pound fiberglass copy of old classic one-man pack model of only 10½-foot length. Grumman rental square-stern aluminum canoes (top left), packed for camping, have Y-shaped transoms for mounting small outboards. Old Town 16-foot Wahoo (left) is shown rigged with sliding rowing seat; sails with leeboards or dagger boards may be added

■ INDIANS AND VOYAGEURS of 400 years ago would surely recognize today's canoes as close relatives of the craft they used to build. But the comparison would stop there as construction and design developments of just the last few years have made these little double-enders much easier and safer to handle, while adding extra years to their life.

No longer is the canoe considered a tippy cockleshell constructed of short-lived canvas and brittle wood. Now there are a variety of models made of fiberglass, marine aluminum, ABS plastic foam and polyethylene. This means that there will be one to fit just about any need you may have.

Basically, the craft is one of the most versatile afloat. It can be paddled, poled, sailed, powered with an outboard motor and some are even rigged for rowing. The one factor that makes a canoe so useful is that a minimum water depth is necessary. This means that it can go almost anywhere.

choosing a canoe

When choosing a canoe, selection is determined by design, features, size and construction material. The purposes for which it will be used will help determine the proper type and size. The material it is made of plus the workmanship is suggested by waters where it will be used, and personal preferences.

Today's standard canoe is pointed at both ends and has a flatter floor than canoes of yesteryear. The flatter floor makes a more stable craft with good load capacity. At the same time this floor will help you paddle and handle the canoe fairly

easily. The ends do not curl up as high and are less likely to catch the wind.

One basic variation to be explored is a squared-off stern. Though a bracket can be clamped on a double-ender to mount an outboard motor at one side, the square stern is more convenient for motor mounting. A standard square stern is more difficult to paddle in fast water than a double-ender, but the Y-stern which is pointed underwater and flares up, paddles easily and is a useful compromise for motors up to about three hp. Some of the big freighter canoes with deep square sterns can handle as much as 20 hp.

canoes for racing, hunting

Additional types include the racing canoe, a long lean model that may be up to 24 feet in length with a beam of only 26 inches. Its sleek form helps it glide swiftly through the water. Quite different are stable, wide-beamed canoes for hunters and fishermen that sometimes mount sponson flotation along each side. Though these clumsier canoes are difficult to paddle in fast water or high winds, they also are difficult to tip over and can even be rowed.

Among specialized narrow-beam models are some resembling kayaks. These are used mainly for river touring and have limited load capacity. Since they are usually decked in, they are not as suitable for long camping trips as hulls with more space for duffel. One new ultra-light miniature is made in fiberglass by Old Town Canoes as a Rushton replica. Pioneer canoe enthusiast Henry Rushton made his 10-foot original of cedar planking. Weighing only 15 pounds 9½ ounces,

Flotation panels along sides of Sportspal aluminum canoes, cartoppers make them especially stable

it was named Nessmuk—the pen name of early wilderness writer George Washington Sears.

Most canoes today have a keel running along the center of the bottom that helps stiffen the hull and fend off abrasion. For paddling lakes and slow rivers, the keel aids in keeping a straight course. In fast white water, however, a keelless hull would be more responsive and maneuverable for the canoeist.

The small canoes—up to 12 feet—are generally one-man models. They are easy to cartop and are popular with fishermen and hunters. One problem of these models though is that they are often less stable and are best left to an expert. One exception to this is the Sportspal, which has a wide beam for greater stability.

Canoes of intermediate length—14 or 15 feet—are often chosen by a beginner who believes that full-size canoes are too long for him. For a long trip, however, they are too long for one man and too short for all the gear needed for two. Another problem is that they will generally ride low in the water when loaded with two men and all their gear. And anyone who has paddled a heavily loaded canoe knows how difficult it can be to paddle. When in doubt, it is frequently wise to

---

CANOE MANUFACTURERS

Among well-known canoe makers are the following:
American Fiber-Lite Inc., Box 67, Marion, Ill. 62959
Country Plastics Corp., 100 Verdi St., Farmingdale, N.Y. 11735
Delhi Mfg., Box 7, Delhi, La. 71232
Grumman Boats, Marathon, N.Y. 13803
Land & Lake Mfg., Box 223, Manchester, Mich. 48158
Michi-Craft Corp, 19995 19 Mile Rd., Big Rapids, Mich. 49307
Old Tówn Canoe Co., Old Town, Me. 04468
Ouachita Marine & Industrial, 721 Main St., Little Rock, Ark. 72201
Sawyer Canoe Co., 234 South State St., Oscoda, Mich. 48750
Sears, Roebuck and Co., Sears Tower, Chicago, Ill. 60684
Small Boat Shop, Box 808, Sandy Hook, Conn. 06482
Smoker-Craft, New Paris, Ind. 46553
Sportspal Inc., Emlenton, Pa. 16373
Trailcraft Inc., Box 606, Concordia, Kans. 66901
Trembly Canoes, 40 St. Paul St., St. Felicien, Que.
Tubbs of Vermont, Forest Dale, Vt. 05745
Voyageur Canoe Co., Millbrook, Ont.
Whitewater Marine Products, Box 355, Indianola, Iowa 50125
Whitmore Corp., 85 Willow St., New Haven, Conn. 06511

Sail, mast, rudder and leeboards convert the 15-foot 3-inch Grumman Sportcanoe into a sailboat. The beamy family boat can also take motor, oars or paddles

buy the next larger size. For a two-man canoe trip of several days up to several weeks, nothing under 16 feet is recommended and 17 feet is better.

Models larger than 18 feet are difficult to cartop and portage, although they have greater stability. Giant square-stern Rupert House 24-foots are still used in Canada's far north by Indians for transportation.

construction materials

Among canoeists, the big controversy comes when construction materials are discussed. Some consider wood canoes to be cooler in summer and warmer in winter than aluminum or fiberglass, easier to repair than aluminum and perhaps even easier than fiberglass. These might be important factors on a wilderness trip through rugged country but not as important for the Sunday afternoon canoeist. Oldtime canoeists rate wood as quieter than aluminum and plastic as well. But a 16-foot model in wood can cost $100 more than one of other material, and the wood has to be varnished and the canvas covering painted.

Aluminum canoes are rated almost maintenance-free and are particularly rugged, although they may dent if they hit a rock or other hard object when traveling fast. Considered slightly hotter and more noisy than other makes, they are also lighter and this plus their good carrying capacity make them popular with canoe trippers.

Canoes built of fiberglass and plastic are classed as less noisy than metal and cooler in a hot summer sun. Like wooden models, they tend to be more elastic and may take a harder blow without puncturing. Some canoe buffs claim plastics are smoother and tend to slide off underwater rocks more easily than aluminum or fabric. Fiberglass is, of course largely maintenance-free and reasonably easy to patch. A disadvantage is that such a canoe must usually be heavier than aluminum in order to be sturdy. ABS plastic foam resists dents and chipping.

But practically all modern models require less push to paddle, have less windage to drift the hull off course and require minimum care.

A beginner is wise to get advice and instruction from an expert when choosing the best model for local waters. He also should learn to paddle it properly plus the techniques of righting and reboarding from the water if it should tip over.

He should remember that new laws require canoeists to carry—or, preferably, wear—life preservers.

Once the basics are mastered, few forms of boating can give more quiet pleasure.

Accessories for canoeing include clamp-on outboard brackets (upper left) from Grumman and others. The 12 and 16-foot wood-and-canvas models above are assembled from Trailcraft kits, maker of fiberglass square and double-end canoe kits as well. At left, Old Town Potomac C-2, a white-water covered two-man model, is 15½-foot fiberglass slalom canoe. The canoeists kneel while the kayak paddlers sit down

New under sail

BY BILL MCKEOWN

Sailboats are slow—but offer
satisfactions of a silent sport that
requires skill, not gas. On these
pages you will find some of the latest
ideas from a surfboard with a
sail to cabin craft for long voyages

■ Boating under sail has received a big push from threatened shortages of gasoline. Both power and sailcraft sales are up recently, but apparently many new boatmen want to try the quiet art of moving with the breeze.

Sailing skills have not changed much in 2000 years, but the boats themselves are very different from those of only 20 years ago. Endless maintenance battles with dry rotted hulls and stretched sails are almost over. Synthetics such as Dacron and nylon have replaced cotton sails and manila lines. Wooden hulls now are rare. Fiberglass-reinforced plastic instead is molded into sailboat shapes. A few notable exceptions are made of

Minifish is AMF Alcort's 75-lb (about $415) mini-copy of world-famous Sailfish, Sunfish, and Force 5

Motor sailers, like Albin 25MS imported by Larsson USA (above), offer advantages of power and sail, twin cabins and popular midships cockpit in a 25-footer. Dinghy sailing (left) can be a challenge for beginner and experienced helmsman alike. Grumman 8½-foot model converts from cat rig to oars, outboard

O'Day Gold Medal 22 can sleep four; power along with an outboard clamped on a transom bracket; draws only two feet with centerboard up. Price: around $3300

Ensenada 20, an even smaller 20-foot example of compact trend, sleeps five, needs only one foot of water, trails easily and sells for about $3500 on West Coast

Chrysler Musketeer offers high-performance speeds. It is designed by Britain's catamaran champion, has trailerable 8-foot beam for day-sailing comfort

Windsurfer, a 12-foot surfboard may just start a completely new sport. This 12-foot surfboard is rigged for sporty stand-up sailing and costs approximately $415 from Windsurfing International, Santa Monica, Calif. The rider shifts his weight to steer the board as he holds onto a rail

Midship 25 from Midship Yachts, Westminster, Calif., offers easy handling with a ketch rig, a midship cockpit, optional swing keel to reduce draft from five feet to one for trailering. Sleeps five. About $8000

Luger Leeward sloop is 16-foot example of a good day-sailer family boat suitable for learning. Craft is built from a molded fiberglass kit selling for about $800. Sloop seats six, has 75-inch beam, draws three feet with centerboard down, weighs 700 lbs. Kits for other sizes also are available

marine aluminum—such as recent America's Cup defenders and challengers.

Most popular rig now, and the easiest with which to learn, is a single mast mounting a pointed-top Marconi mainsail plus a jib stepped in a 12 to 15-foot hull with adjustable centerboard or fixed keel. The little sloop is likely to have topsides high enough to keep passengers safely aboard, provide enough action without threatening constantly to capsize, and prove seaworthy in moderate airs and sheltered seas. Smaller boats are not safer or easier to sail. The Sailfish, a sailing surfboard first launched 25 years ago, and all its thousands of successors and imitators, are great fun to sail but easy to flip and require more skill. Tricky also are powerboats and other craft rigged for sail but not designed for wind power. Without keel or leeboards, they are unstable and tend to slide downwind.

sailors carry outboards now

Power, however, is no longer scoffed at by sail skippers, and a small outboard to provide an auxiliary push when desired is often stowed aboard.

The lateen sail of sailboards and single triangle or gaff-headed rig of sailing dinghies and catboats is usually reserved for smaller craft. Multimasted yawl, ketch and occasionally schooner rigs are sometimes found on yachts of about 30 feet and up.

Newly popular are cabin craft for slow cruising and multihull catamarans and trimarans for fast planing. Today's sailor can get much more action afloat and fewer maintenance chores and less expense ashore.

Herreshoff Eagle provides pleasures and lines of a character boat with easy maintenance of modern fiberglass. Clipper bow and gaff-headed rig of little 22-foot pocket packet combine with wheel steering, outboard well for auxiliary power, bunks for two. It sells, complete with sails, for about $8000

Folding sailboat

This portable sailing boat
folds for toting. Weighing only 50 pounds,
it collapses into a flat
surfboard-like package to fit on your car

■ FOLDING BOATS aren't new, but this classy little 9-foot sailing dory promises to be one of the fastest to assemble and most versatile to operate. The 50-pound Porta-Bote goes together in minutes and collapses into a slim, flat, surfboard-like package for easy cartopping. With its sail removed, it becomes a rowboat for fishing, a small outboard or a camouflage-covered floating duck blind for hunters. Its skin is of tough, tear-resistant polypropylene with built-in foam flotation to prevent sinking. Assembly is merely a matter of unfolding two hinged halves and inserting seats that act as spreaders (right). For sailing, there's a slip-on rudder and pivoted leeboards that swing up out of the way. About $460 complete with sail rig, $280 without sail. K Enterprises, Box 2287, Menlo Park, California 94025.

Sander-grinder sharpens almost anything

Foley's newest grinder has pulleys for greater safety—direct drive eliminates the drive belts. It's available with a floor stand, double-extended shaft motor and light

BY HARRY WICKS

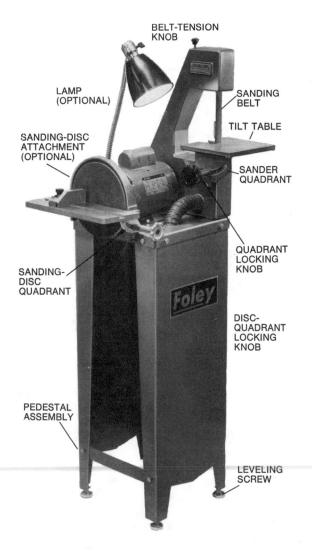

BELT-TENSION KNOB

LAMP (OPTIONAL)

SANDING-DISC ATTACHMENT (OPTIONAL)

SANDING BELT

TILT TABLE

SANDER QUADRANT

SANDING-DISC QUADRANT

QUADRANT LOCKING KNOB

Foley

DISC-QUADRANT LOCKING KNOB

PEDESTAL ASSEMBLY

LEVELING SCREW

■ IF YOU DON'T YET own a sander/grinder, you're in for a treat when you finally do add this versatile piece of equipment to your complement of shop tools. With one you can sand fine work accurately, and sharpen just about every cutting edge you have around your home and shop.

The tool shown is the latest from Foley Manufacturing Co., of Minneapolis. The belt-sander pulleys are enclosed in a sturdy, die-cast aluminum housing for optimum safety, and the tool operates with direct drive from the motor shaft to eliminate possible belt-drive dangers. You can purchase just the sander/grinder and mount it on your workbench, or add such optional extras as floor stand, double-extended shaft motor and disc sander, or light.

little assembly required

Model 311 arrives from the manufacturer practically fully assembled—you simply put together the major components.

The first task on my test agenda was to do some grinding using the 1x42-in. sanding belt. I quickly restored the edges on a number of items including circular-saw blades, chisels, plane iron and scissors. The tool sharpens efficiently, runs quietly, and the belt tracks without a hitch.

Next, I used the 8-in. sanding-disc attachment to smooth some rough stock. Again, the tool performed beautifully. Then, after squaring the disc table with the disc and adjusting the quadrant pointer to zero, I made a number of passes with the miter gauge to check accuracy when sanding mitered cuts. The results were excellent—they were on the mark every time.

A good feature is the consideration given to dust collection. A short length of hose from the grinder housing passes down through the table; at the outboard end you simply connect your shop vacuum hose.

All key points considered—safety, performance and tool construction—I rate model 311 a good buy. For the price, though, I think one refinement that might have been included on the optional floor stand is leveling casters instead of leveling screws. I'd rather roll than lift or slide the tool. Perhaps that is nit-picking, but as for sharpening and grinding, it's a dandy.

Motor: ½ hp, 3450 rpm, 115 v.
Worktable height (optional equipment): 40 in.
Overall height: 51 in.
Worktable size: 7x8 in.
Abrasive-belt size 1x42 in.
Pulley bearings: ball
Net weight: 71 lbs.   Shipping weight: 76 lbs.
Prices: Basic sander/grinder, $161.50. Machine with a double extended-shaft: motor and disc sander is $213. F.o.b. manufacturer: Foley Manufacturing Co., 3300 Fifth St., Minneapolis, Minn. 55418.

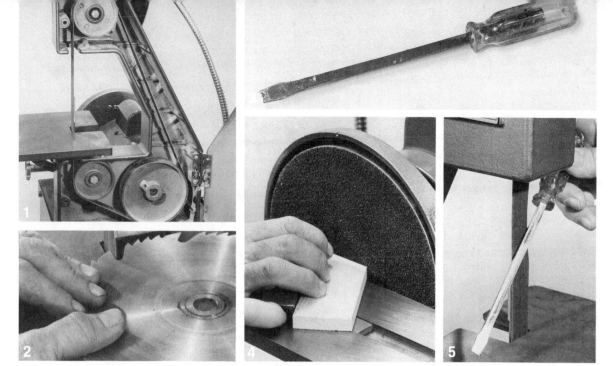

It's a workhorse, says the author. The door is swung open (photo 1) to expose the machine's innards. The belt revolves around a single roller at the top and two at the bottom. Sawdust is drawn into a vacuum through a small hole below the left roller at the bottom. Typical shop chores: Sharpening a circular saw blade (2); using the optional sanding disc on a miter cut (4). An old beat-up screwdriver (3) is being renewed by the belt sander (5)

Mounted on its floor stand, the grinder is particularly comfortable to work at. Most of the time, the operator can sit on a stool as he works

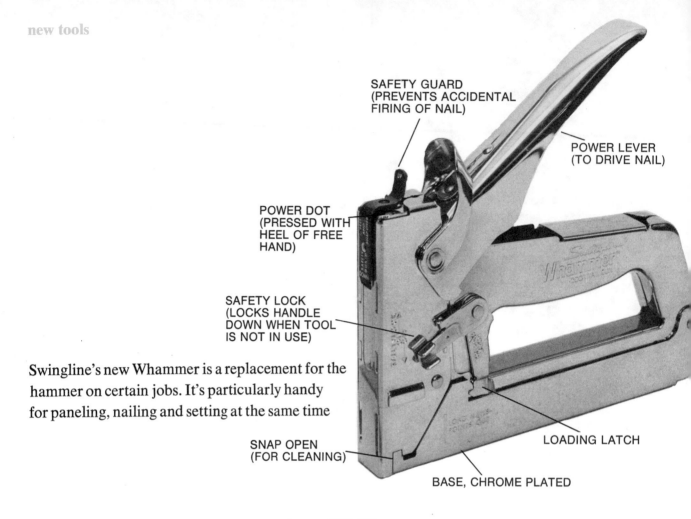

SAFETY GUARD
(PREVENTS ACCIDENTAL
FIRING OF NAIL)

POWER LEVER
(TO DRIVE NAIL)

POWER DOT
(PRESSED WITH
HEEL OF FREE
HAND)

SAFETY LOCK
(LOCKS HANDLE
DOWN WHEN TOOL
IS NOT IN USE)

Swingline's new Whammer is a replacement for the hammer on certain jobs. It's particularly handy for paneling, nailing and setting at the same time

SNAP OPEN
(FOR CLEANING)

LOADING LATCH

BASE, CHROME PLATED

Wham goes the Whammer

BY HARRY WICKS

■ I APPROACHED THIS SHOP TEST with a degree of skepticism. Since my 16-oz. claw hammer seems almost to be an extension of my arm on any shop or home-improvement project, I wondered how a "stapler" could possibly replace "old faithful." After a couple of workshop sessions and a day of paneling, I learned the Whammer could, indeed, outperform the hammer on certain tasks.

Basically, the Whammer operates on the lever principle. When the handle is operated, an internal ram is lifted and then driven forward by a ram spring. To use the gun, you simply position the tool, place the heel of your free hand against the Power Dot on the head, and squeeze off a nail. This two-handed technique gives comfortable position, while holding the gun's shoe flat and firm against the work. After each nail is driven, the handle is then allowed to raise itself and the gun is ready for the next drive.

For openers, I test-drove a dozen or so nails

into the hardboard paneling in my workshop. The nails went in easily and were well set (countersunk). This feature I liked because it saves time. Rather than having to rap each nail with nailset and hammer as you go, you just move on to the next nail position. In addition to saving time, the gun avoids the "union marks"—made by a nailset that slipped or an errant hammer—which frequently identify do-it-yourself workmanship.

Loading the tool is easier than an ordinary staple gun because, unlike staples, the Whammer nails are held together by an almost invisible glue. You simply open the gun, slide in a strip of 100 nails, close the gun and fire away.

Though specifically designed for use with wood paneling, the nail gun has, I found, other good uses. It's extra-handy when assembling small bench projects which call for the use of brads. Also it is useful on those projects in which the glue and joints will primarily hold the finished project together (such as the box shown at right with

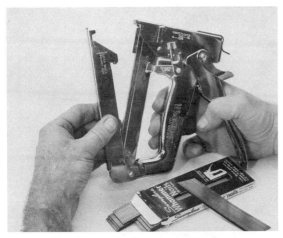

Loading is easy. The latch is pulled back (top) to open the bottom and a strip of 100 nails is slipped into the gun (above). The bottom is then closed and the gun is ready to use

dovetail-joint corners). Here, several well-set nails were "whammed" to hold the box rigid while the glue dried.

If there is any fault, it is that the gun will jam if a nail strikes a particularly dense object such as a knot or metal fixture. However, the gun is easily cleared by flipping open the bottom plate and aiming the gun downward. Gravity usually takes over and the nail drops out. If the bottom plate resists opening after a jam, you simply pull back on the loading latch, insert the safety guard in front of the latch and turn the guard down on the bottom plate.

SPECIFICATIONS—Whammer 2001 Nail Gun	
Operation	Used according to instructions, it drives and sets nails with one stroke.
Nails	Brad-type Whammer 2001 nails only. Available in 1-1/32-in. length, 18-gauge galvanized, in four wood-tone colors.
Price	Gun (with 1000 nails), $19.95; nails per package of 1000, $1.95.
Manufacturer	Swingline, Div. of Swingline, Inc., 32-00 Skillman Ave, Long Island City, N.Y. 11101.

Casing can be applied using the gun. Notice the left-hand position to keep the shoe flat

The Whammer shines on a paneling job. Scratches are avoided by lifting the gun after nailing

The tool is handy at the workbench, too. Here it is used to assemble a small tissue box

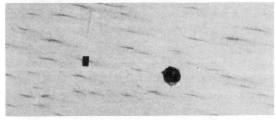

A test comparing a Whammer nail and a 4d finishing nail. The former is less obvious

The safety guard, which locks the ram, is removed to use the gun. It should always be replaced to avoid an accidental firing of the gun

DOUBLE-INSULATED HOUSING

CHAIN-OIL FILL KNOB

REMINGTON ELECTRIC LIMB N'TRIM
PATENT PENDING

GUIDE-BAR NUT

TWO-PRONG PLUG

CHAIN

GUIDE BAR

Pint-size chain saw

BY HARRY WICKS

■ AT FIRST GLANCE, this mini chain saw looks more like a toy than a tool. I found that looks can be deceiving, though—this tool is anything but a toy. Called Limb N'Trim Electric by its maker, Remington Chain Saws, it's priced most reasonably around $35.

Though not designed for all-day log-cutting sessions, the saw I used performed without a hitch recently on some typical do-it-yourself backyard chores. Mostly, I used it to slice small-diameter logs for firewood and to trim dead branches from several trees and bushes.

Powered by a 1¾-hp electric motor, the tool runs considerably quieter than the loud gas-powered type. The noise level is about what you'd expect from a 7 or 8-in. portable circular saw.

The maker doesn't claim it to be a heavy-duty saw for big-tree felling and the like, but it does make quick work of around-the-yard light chores most homeowners will want such a tool for. It also provides a lightweight and quick-cutting saw for homeowners who tackle do-it-yourself building projects. Its 8-in. cutting capacity is sufficient to do a surprising number of jobs, and its weight is a comfortable-to-handle 6¾ pounds.

takes minutes to assemble

As most chain saws do, it comes with guide bar and chain unmounted. Assembly takes just minutes, and then you simply plug in the tool and go to work. There are two musts when using this tool: A 50-ft. 16-gauge extension cord is the minimum size recommended for safe operation. Second, you must oil the chain manually by depressing the oil-filler knob at least once each time you begin a new cut.

I'd like to see that oil-filler knob relocated slightly. I found the repeated stretching of my left thumb from the support handle to it was a bit tiring. Admittedly, I'm splitting hairs over a minor point. At about $35, the Limb N'Trim is a dandy tool for anyone who wants a chain saw without a price tag which is completely out of reach. After all, a big gas-powered model will mean you have to shell out $100 or more. But when using the Limb N'Trim, be realistic, don't expect it to perform as its more expensive cousins do.

SPECIFICATIONS
Limb N'Trim Electric Chain Saw

Weight: 6¾ lbs.
Guide bar length: 8 in.
Cutting capacity: 8 in.
Motor rating: 1¾ hp
Motor voltage: 115 v.a.c.
Cycles: 60
Alternator rating: 1500 watts
No-load sprocket speed: 4500 rpm
Price: $34.95

Manual chain oiler, double-insulated housing. Manufacturer: Remington Chain Saws, Desa Industries, Inc., Power Product Div., 25000 South Western Ave., Park Forest, Ill. 60466.

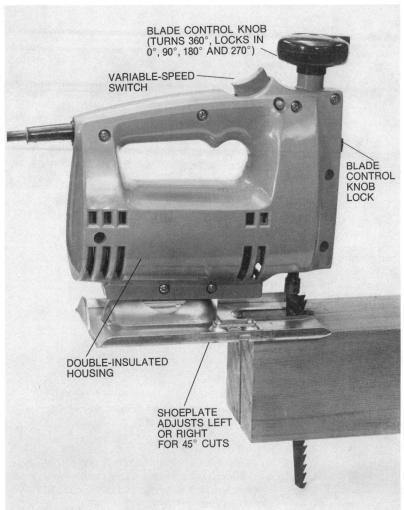

BLADE CONTROL KNOB
(TURNS 360°, LOCKS IN
0°, 90°, 180° AND 270°)

VARIABLE-SPEED
SWITCH

BLADE
CONTROL
KNOB
LOCK

DOUBLE-INSULATED
HOUSING

SHOEPLATE
ADJUSTS LEFT
OR RIGHT
FOR 45° CUTS

The combination of a rotating blade and a thumb-controlled variable speed allows Wen's Model 531 Scroller Saw to negotiate the trickiest cutting lines easily

Scroll-cutting sabre saw

SPECIFICATIONS—Wen Model 51 Sabre Saw

Motor: 4-amp., ⅔ hp. Rated heavy duty by maker.
Blade: Rotates 360°, can be locked in four positions—0°, 90°, 180° and 270°.
Variable speed: 0 to 2800 strokes per minute. Locks in two speed positions—intermediate and full.
Housing: Unbreakable, double-insulated, has lifetime guarantee.
Bearings: Lifetime-lubricated bronze and needle bearings.
Shoeplate: Adjusts right or left for 45° cutting.
Price: About $40.
Manufacturer: Wen Products, Inc., 5810 Northwest Hwy., Chicago, Ill. 60631.

BY HARRY WICKS

■ A COUPLE of interesting features justify a shop test of Wen's Model 531 Scroller Sabre Saw, even though it's not spanking new. Most intriguing is the rotating blade controlled by a knob at the top. This is a good feature on tight turns—because you turn the blade only—but I found it a bit stubborn to work with and, at times, difficult to adjust. The tool's strong feature is its variable-speed range. The speed is controlled manually by varying pressure on a thumb-button switch. Conclusion: Try it in the store; if you like the tool's heft, it's a buy at about $40.

DREMEL'S HANDY new foot control governs the speed of power tools and appliances. When foot is released, a spring moves the treadle to the lowest speed position. Model 217 has an outlet for a 3-prong plug at the back, handles up to 5 amps when controlling motors and up to 600 watts for lights, glue guns, soldering guns, etc. It sells for about $22

New for your shop

THE FAMILIAR BAR CLAMP is updated as Jet Clamps, with spring-loaded jamming wedges that allow instantaneous adjustment and lock firmly when clamping force is applied. A knob on one arm tightens the clamp. The unit is supplied with four sets of interchangeable pads for different kinds of work, including right-angle pads for clamping edges, and a 12-in bar. The English-made clamp is about $29 from Seawood, Inc., 5100 Edina Industrial Blvd., Minneapolis, Minn. 55435

FOR MANICURING the edges of walks and around trees, fences and shrubs, Rockwell now offers a two-in-one lawn tool that you can convert from an edger (top) to a rotary trimmer (bottom) merely by rotating its head 90°. The tool comes with a 6¼-in. blade and a 2.4-ampere motor. It weighs only 7½ lbs., is double-insulated and has a long handle for painless no-stoop trimming. The price: about $30

TO SAVE YOUR ACHING BACK, there's a unique concrete mixer for do-it-yourselfers that lets you mix over 100 pounds of concrete in as little as two minutes simply by wheeling it around like a cart. Called Roll-a-mix, it has a one-piece, 20-in.-dia. drum molded of high-density polyethylene and fitted with a tire to make it serve as a wheel. It's about $60 from Tri-ment Co., 1018 Bloomfield Ave., West Caldwell, N.J. 07006

YOUR POWER DRILL can be even more versatile with this chisel attachment. Stanley Tools' Electrichisel cuts mortise and tenon joints, open dado joints and rabbet joints, to name a few. The ring-around accessory tool (above) is adjustable with an Allen wrench (comes with the tool) for depth control. The tool is available at hardware stores in ½ and ¾-in. sizes for about $5.25 and $5.50

A COMPACT TOOL designed for cutting and finishing plastic and plastic-laminate surfaces, the Arlyn-Cutter has adjustable solid carbide cutters for scoring the workpiece and beveling the edges. According to the manufacturer, the tool can cut in either direction, flush against a wall, and into a corner. It adjusts for various cutting thicknesses. For longer tool life, a light coat of silicone is recommended. From Arlyn/Industries, 6921 Stride Ave., Burnaby 3, B. C.

THE TRICKY SANDER is used in either a straight or bowed position to sand lathe work and hard-to-reach spots. Abrasive cloth, secured by two thumbscrews, holds the spring-steel blade in a bent position. The sander comes with a supply of abrasive strips in three grits. It also accepts standard rolls of emery cloth. About $4.50 from Nicol Tools, Inc., 1047 Raymond Ave., St. Paul, Minn. 55108

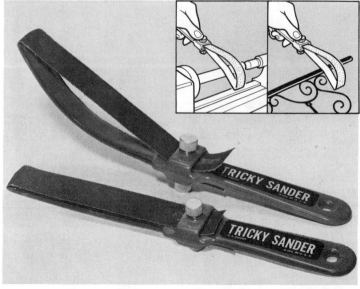

Tripods aren't always tripods

BY *IVAN BERGER*

If you find your tripod too awkward
to carry around for every photographic situation,
take a look at these ingenious alternatives

MIIDA
ELEVATOR
TRI-CLAMP,
$29.75

CAPRO MINI-CLAMP, $6.95

KAISER
MINI-KLETTE,
$9.95
(LEGS RETRACTED)

LINHOF
HEAVY-
DUTY
CLAMPOD
WITH
TREE SCREW,
$54.50

Clamps turn anything into a tripod, fix
camera to doors, furniture, fences, car
bumpers; some (Capro, Kaiser, Linhof)
even screw into trees for secure mounting

Accura Vacuum Camera Support has trig-
ger-operated suction-cup base, adjusts
several inches up and down; about $16

Cameras aren't all that these clamps
and mini-tripods can hold. Here the
Camera-Grabber doubles as a flash stand

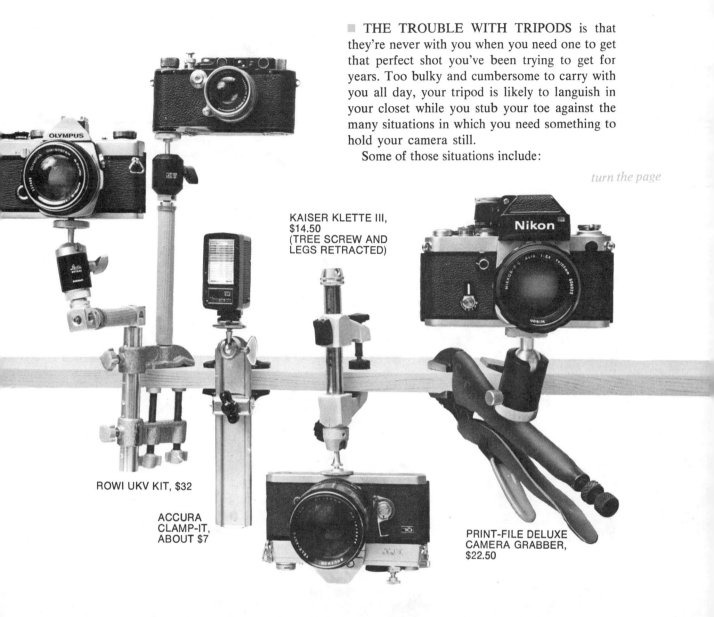

■ THE TROUBLE WITH TRIPODS is that they're never with you when you need one to get that perfect shot you've been trying to get for years. Too bulky and cumbersome to carry with you all day, your tripod is likely to languish in your closet while you stub your toe against the many situations in which you need something to hold your camera still.

Some of those situations include:

turn the page

KAISER KLETTE III, $14.50 (TREE SCREW AND LEGS RETRACTED)

ROWI UKV KIT, $32

ACCURA CLAMP-IT, ABOUT $7

PRINT-FILE DELUXE CAMERA GRABBER, $22.50

Rowi UKV kit (below, right and directly above) costs around $32—plus about $15 for its optional leather case (not shown), but its 18 pieces will adapt readily to a wide and weird variety of purposes and applications. Two such configurations are shown here—but you can imagine many more from the disassembled view of all the parts

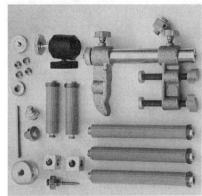

Mini tripods fit your pocket or camera bag

Mini tripods are easy to carry, work in situations
where standard tripods won't. Of those shown, Miida,
Bolex and Kati II are height-adjustable; Minox is
most compact; Bolex, Miida and Leitz are most versatile

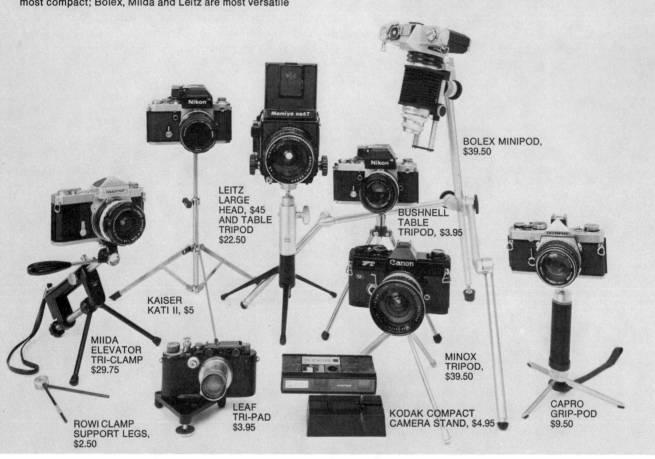

BOLEX MINIPOD,
$39.50

LEITZ
LARGE
HEAD, $45
AND TABLE
TRIPOD
$22.50

BUSHNELL
TABLE
TRIPOD, $3.95

KAISER
KATI II, $5

MIIDA
ELEVATOR
TRI-CLAMP
$29.75

ROWI CLAMP
SUPPORT LEGS,
$2.50

LEAF
TRI-PAD
$3.95

KODAK COMPACT
CAMERA STAND, $4.95

MINOX
TRIPOD,
$39.50

CAPRO
GRIP-POD
$9.50

Alpa Macrostat system is versatile, expensive but you can
buy just the pieces you need. The outfit at right includes
Stabil miniature tripod (about $120), plus components worth
about $110. Outdoor outfit above includes large and small
ground-spike, mirror reflector, other components, about $80

Built for telescopes, Bushnell Shooters Stand (about $28) needs ball-joint head (Leitz head is shown) for camera use. Height can be increased with extension

Adjustable ball-joint heads let you angle mini-tripods to rest them against your chest or vertical surfaces. The Cappo Grip-Pod is shown in the photograph

- Time exposures.
- Closeups.
- Shooting Kodachrome on overcast days.
- As emergency flash or reflector stands.
- Keeping the camera aimed while you set the self-timer and get in the shot yourself.

The problem may seem a difficult one, but it is not insoluble. The stores are full of tripods that fold small enough to fit your gadget bag or pocket, clamps that convert any handy objects into camera supports (fence rails or your car door, for example), even supports built especially for use in your automobile.

We've tried all the gadgets shown on these pages except the Questar car-mount and the Accura vacuum pod, and here are our favorites:
- Minox—high-priced, but by far the easiest to carry. (It would be even easier if it had a pocket clip.)
- Miida—very versatile (it doubles as a clamp or

Bolex's "praying mantis" Minipod adjusts to many different applications as shown here and on next page. It folds to 12 inches long, weighs 22 ounces and comes with its own carrying case and shoulder strap

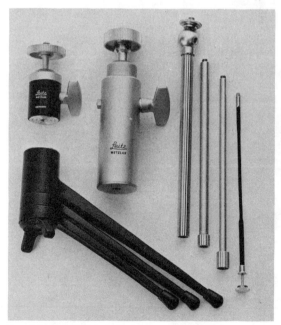

Two tripods: Stable Leitz (shown with ball-joint heads for about $22.50 and $45) swivels shut for pocketing or to double as tele handgrip. Minox's three sections and cable release fit inside one another

Turn your car into a camera dolly

Bolex Minipod again, here braced against a car dashboard for over-the-hood shots. Adjusted differently, it can hook over bumper for low-angle dolly shots

Questar Carpod (around $43.50) is designed to fit all cars. It was designed by Dr. R. C. Ashley, who used it to shoot birds from the roadside, in comfort

Rowi Car Camera Support (about $22), grips windshield with suction cup, adjusts to windshield angle. In our tests, it held a camera securely for days. An excellent choice for a car-mounted movie camera

tripod) but recently discontinued; so if you want one, look for a store that has some old stock.
• Leitz—a classic: *very* solid, folds flat, and doubles as a pistol grip for long tele lenses. Leica quality all the way.
• Bolex Minipod—you'll never figure out *all* the tricks it can do; obviously the work of a very good, mad genius who had lots of different camera positions on his mind.
• Rowi car mount—makes very steady movies. It has a suction cup which adjusts to the windshield angle and holds the cameras securely in place for days on end.
• Bushnell Table Tripod—sturdy, and a steal at around $4.
• Rowi UKV—like an Erector set, it seems to do just about everything.

The various Questar, Leaf and Bushnell models sell by mail. The other ones you should be able to get through your dealer.

Bushnell Car Window Mount has soft jaws that clamp over window glass, sturdy pan head. Like Bushnell Shooter's Stand (previous page), it's very solid

New aids for photo drying

■ DRYING CAN BE one of the most irksome aspects of darkroom work: Minutes ago you were busy developing, and now there's nothing you can do but sit and wait until your negatives are ready to print, or your prints can be shown without dripping.

To alleviate the frustration a little, the drum dryer to the left can speed up print drying, without requiring all the storage space such dryers usually need. The dryer below does the same for film. If you are using the quick-drying resin-coated papers you will need a special dryer. The one at the right below holds several prints safely till they air-dry.

Brooks Space-Saver dries prints up to 10x12, and can handle up to 30 8x10s an hour. Like the big, professional dryers, it's motorized, has a nonadjustable thermostatic heat control that keeps the drum surface at about 200° F. Unlike big dryers, though, it folds in seconds to take up only 11½ x 18 inches of shelf space and sits only 12¾ inches high. From Burleigh Brooks (44 Burlews Court, Hackensack, N.J. 07601), it takes 600 watts, costs about $125

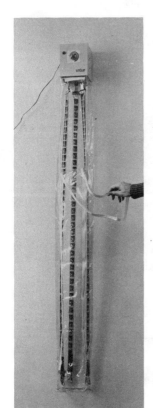

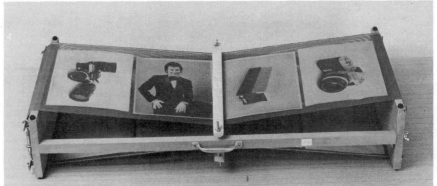

Depth of Field "Open Air" print-dryer (above) holds prints flat between taut layers of plastic screening while they air-dry. Model 15 (shown) holds 16 8x10s or 8 11x14s, and costs about $24; attache-case-sized Model 10 holds eight 8x10s and costs about $18. Either model can be rested on end, on edge or stacked. Also available is a blower attachment designed for quicker drying at a cost of around $25. All prices plus $2 postage from Depth of Field, Box 141, Madison, Wis. 53703

Prinz Jet (left) takes roll film, not prints. Warmed, filtered air bathes up to three rolls of film, which hang straight to prevent end-to-end curl. A timer shuts it off. It's priced at approximately $45 plus shipping from Bass Camera, 179 West Madison, Chicago, Ill. 60602

Steady...aim...shoot!

The gunstocks, pistol grips and other gadgets shown here help keep your camera steady, even when you're using one of those long telephoto lenses

BY IVAN BERGER

■ HOLDING A CAMERA steady is a tripod's job. But holding a camera steady while you move it is another problem—and a common one for users of telephoto lenses and for movie makers. Here's a variety of gadgets that will help.

Gunstocks turn your camera into a rifle, giving

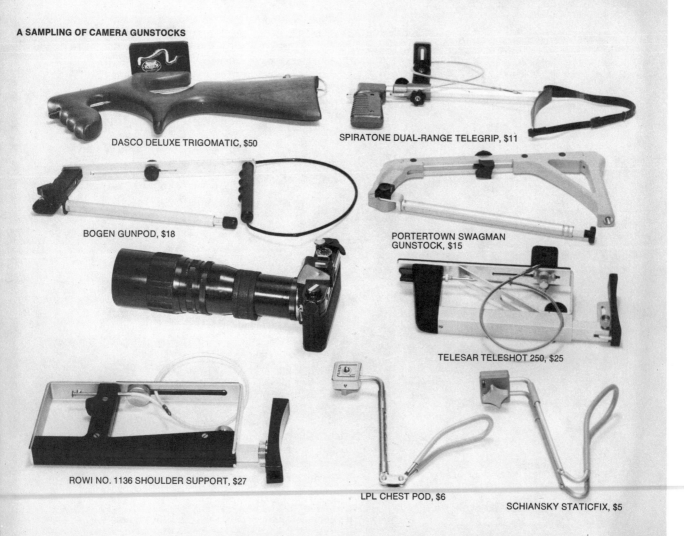

A SAMPLING OF CAMERA GUNSTOCKS

DASCO DELUXE TRIGOMATIC, $50

SPIRATONE DUAL-RANGE TELEGRIP, $11

BOGEN GUNPOD, $18

PORTERTOWN SWAGMAN GUNSTOCK, $15

TELESAR TELESHOT 250, $25

ROWI NO. 1136 SHOULDER SUPPORT, $27

LPL CHEST POD, $6

SCHIANSKY STATICFIX, $5

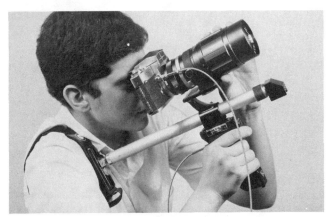

The Swagman gunstock converts to a "riflepod" (above) with clamp-on inverted-Y-shaped legs. The bottom crossbar also swings down and telescopes (right) to form a monopod-like foot. It's about $15 from Porter's Camera, Box 628, Cedar Falls, Iowa 50613. The Bogen gunpod also has a swing-down leg

The LPL chestpod folds compactly, has 90° side tilt for vertical-format pictures and expands from 6½ to 9 inches in height. The Schiansky Staticfix, otherwise similar, does not have the special features

The most gunlike, the Dasco Trigomatic was also the most comfortable (and the most costly, at about $50, for this deluxe version). It needs a tripod thread adapter for most cameras

The Soligor shoulder bracket's handle attaches to a camera bracket or the front of a telescoping rod, or it can be used as a pistol grip. It sells for about $45

The Rowi No. 1136 shoulder bracket collapses into a very compact rectangle. This Questar version sells for around $21

For extra bracing, the Peter-Lisand shoulder brace rests on the shoulder and waist. This is the $100 professional movie version

The Rowi chainpod is a small plastic tube with two tripod-screw endcaps connected by a long chain. Screw one to the camera and pull up. It steadies the camera amazingly and only costs about $3

Unipods take less than one-third the weight and bulk of tripods. This Miida version has a hidden secret (above right): three short steadying legs within the tube. Unfold them and step on one for steadiness. The three-section version extends to 60 inches and costs about $21. The 66-inch four-section version is around $23. Another version, Accura's five-section zoompod, expands to 58 inches and costs about $18

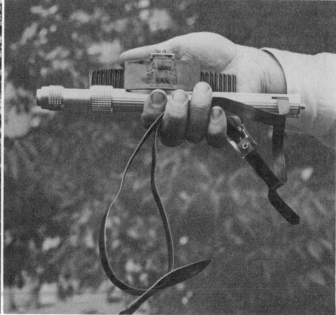

The Testrite beltpod uses your neck, hands and belt (above left) as steadying points. Folded (above right), it's a mere handful, and so's its price: $8

Pistol grips give quick aim with short lenses. This Patterson model sells for about $11 with cable release

The versatile Miida pistol grip can fix under or on either side of a camera; side-mounted, its shoe holds the flash for better-angled lighting. The outfit has a price tag of $22, exclusive of the second cable release, which is extra

The Accura Store-A-Grip serves as a camera handle and flash holder and holds two rolls of film. About $10

The Sunset Master Grip, with built-in cable release, comes in 35-mm ($20) and 2¼ x2¼ -inch ($21) sizes

The Kilfitt Kigrip has a removable shoulder rest, so it can double as a shoulder-pod or pistol grip. It's about $60 from Karl Heitz

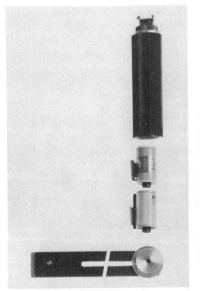

you complete freedom of movement, yet they still reduce camera shake. They vary widely, so try one for size before buying any. Chestpods are more compact, but harder to use.

Monopods are lighter and more compact than tripods. If they're tall enough to bring the camera's eyepiece up to your eye while you stand normally, their one leg and your two legs become a fairly steady "tripod"—but again, you should try it for size if you're tall.

Pistol grips beneath the camera are good for quick-draw shooting; beneath a telephoto lens with its own tripod socket, they act like very compact gunpods.

Likable little Leica

BY IVAN BERGER

■ MY BASIC VACATION-PHOTO outfit has always included a camera with through-the-lens light meter, a wide-angle, a tele and a fast normal lens—plus a stiff shoulder from hauling it all around. But just such an outfit—the new Leica CL with 40-mm f/2 wide-angle/normal and 90-mm f/4 tele lenses—can be cradled in my palm.

The CL will take most bayonet-mount Leica "M" lenses (or older Leica-thread lenses, with adapters). However, the two lenses shown were designed, like the CL itself, for compactness; not just because they're smaller than earlier Leica lenses, but because one of them—the 40-mm—is designed to take the place of both a 35-mm wide-angle and a fast 50-mm normal lens.

And the CL's finder system was designed to match those lenses. Bayonet in the 90-mm, and a bright frame in the finder shows you just the 90-mm field; bayonet in the 40-mm, and the finder shows you fields for it and for 50-mm lenses. Unlike earlier Leica Ms (and Leitz's current M5 model), there are no frames for 35-mm or 135-mm lenses, though you can use them with external finders.

The rangefinder isn't perfectly suited to all other lenses, either. Keeping the camera compact required a shorter measuring base and less finder magnification than on "M" Leicas. That makes the CL less suitable for lenses longer than its 90-mm, or faster than its 40-mm f/2.

Obviously, the CL isn't as versatile as a single-lens reflex. But it has advantages over an SLR, too. Not only is it smaller and lighter, but it's quieter (no mirror flap) and focuses easily and accurately.

As with most of today's SLRs you'll find exposure information in the finder window. And, as in a few reflexes, you'll find a shutter-speed scale there, too.

Like most rangefinder cameras, the CL is a better action camera than an SLR. Its focusing is, for most people, quicker and more precise than a reflex's, the image doesn't disappear at the moment of exposure, and you can see around the edge of the bright frame.

The camera may be compact, but the price isn't: with 40-mm f/2 lens, the CL is about $500 its 90-mm lens is about $250.

Complete CL outfit—camera with normal/wide-angle 40-mm f/2 lens and 90-mm f/4 telephoto—nestles easily in palm of hand, can cover a wide range of situations

Size comparison (below) with earlier Leica M2 shows both CL body and lenses smaller, despite built-in meter. But shorter rangefinder (arrows) is a limitation (see text), and size may be too small for some. Viewfinder (bottom) shows shutter speed (top), meter (right) and fields for 50-mm, new 40-mm lenses. Inserting 90-mm lens switches frame to cover 90-mm field

New for the photographer

Vivitar's tiny Model 50 flash is too small and light to ever leave behind, gets up to 200 flashes from the 6-volt Flatpack battery shown (left), has a K25 guide number of 22, costs about $12. But it's nonautomatic and fits hot-shoe cameras only. Vivitar 272 with bounce-tilt head is an automatic flash with a range of 3 f-stops, thyristor circuit for longer battery life, and a K25 guide number of 50. It sells for approximately $90

As cameramakers get more accustomed to the 110 pocket-cartridge format, their designs grow more sophisticated. For example: Keystone's Pocket-Matic 303 (top) has close-up lens for shots from 3 to 5 feet; Canon's 110 ED (bottom) has rangefinder focusing from 7½ inches to infinity and an f/2 lens—and can print the date on a corner of each picture. Rollei's A110 (center), collapses between shots; electric eye on flash

For those times when everyone wants to get into the picture, including you, Kalimar Mirror Self-Finder can be clipped to accessory shoe on camera and picture taken using a self-timer and tripod. Finder lets you check framing from front of camera. Has frames for 35, 50 and 58-mm lenses. Porter's, 2002 College St., Cedar Falls, Iowa 50613

Newest of the pocket-sized movie cameras, this Yashica Electro —8 Macro has an f/1.9, 9-30-mm manual zoom lens with through-the-lens viewing and a minimum focus distance of only 8½ inches. This close distance will allow you to really zoom in on small objects for a clear view. The price of this movie camera is approximately $160. An optional command set, also at around $160, has a transmitter and receiver for remote radio control so you can actually work the camera from a distance. It also has a time-lapse attachment for intervals of ½ to 60 seconds between frames for creating special-effects or making an automated movie

Audio-Technica AT20SL

Those fabulous new phono cartridges

These new phono cartridges were designed to reproduce
4-channel sound. We put them through an exhaustive series of tests to determine
their quality. Here are the results and what they mean

BY HANS FANTEL

■ THE NEW FOUR-CHANNEL records are causing a revolution in phonograph cartridge design. Just a few years ago, only exceptional phono cartridges could "read" recorded frequencies as high as 20,000 Hz—the average limit of good human hearing—and only exceptional records went that high.

Now, frequencies you can't hear—up to 50,000 Hz—are becoming common on some records, and the super-cartridges to pick up those frequencies are coming in a flood.

But why use frequencies you can't hear?

On the new four-channel "Quadradisc" records recorded with the CD-4 system, these frequencies carry the different signals that eventually are used to sort out the front-channel signals from the rear ones. Matrix four-channel records (using the SQ or QS systems) encode their rear-channel signals differently, without high-frequency carriers—and without as much front-to-rear separation, either. And stereo discs, of course, with no rear channels, also need no carriers.

The cartridges tested for this report are among the first available for playing this new kind of disc —and they give superb results on stereo, as well. But, fine as they are, they're also expensive: The nine models we tested (see chart, page 56), range in price from $65 to $175, with a median price just under $100 (though the one we liked best didn't cost that much).

So, should you now rush out and buy one of these supercartridges? The answer is yes—*if* you're setting up for CD-4 four-channel records now, or if you plan to switch your system to CD-4 in the near future and now need a new cartridge anyway. You might also consider one if you plan to buy CD-4 records now, to prevent the wear that a stereo stylus, which can't move fast enough to follow the high-frequency carrier modulations, will inflict on them. CD-4 records can theoretically be played quadraphonically after even 100 playings with a stereo cartridge, but how well depends on the carrier-frequency response of the CD-4 cartridge and the sensitivity of the demodulator used to convert the cartridge's two output signals into four. Noise may increase and rear-channel sepa-

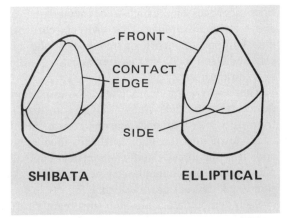

Multiradial styli like the Shibata (above, left) or B&O's Paramanik (at right in the photo below) have smaller contact radii at the sides to trace Quadradiscs' tiny carrier modulations, but larger contact areas to allow higher tracking forces

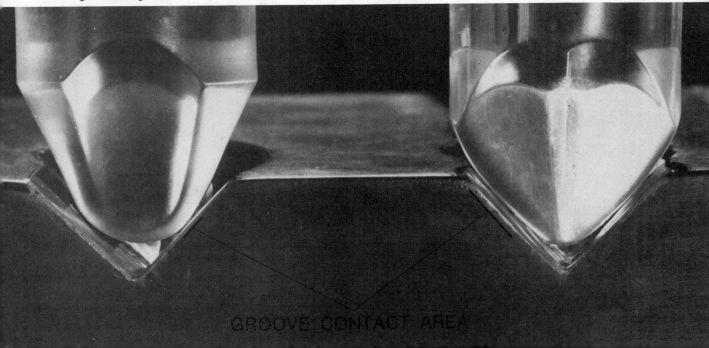

GROOVE CONTACT AREA

ADC Super-XLM

Audio-Technica AT12S

Audio-Technica AT15S

Bang & Olufsen 60

ration decrease noticeably.

And if all you want is the best possible stereo sound, you should definitely consider the top CD-4 cartridges along with the top stereo models for sheer sound quality.

All this talk of "carriers" and "demodulators" is clearer if we explain how CD-4 works. Where matrix quadraphonic discs (like SQ and QS) mix both rear channels into each of the front channels relying on minute differences in signal timing as clues for their eventual decoding into four signals again, CD-4 Quadradiscs are "discrete"—that is, they each contain four distinct signals, two on each wall of the groove.

One of these signals is an audible sum of front and rear channels (left-front plus left-rear on one side of the groove, right-front plus right-rear on the other).

Each groove wall contains, in addition to its front-plus-rear sum, a front-minus-rear difference signal—but you can't hear it. Using a trick invented years ago by telephone engineers to carry

several conversations simultaneously on the same wire, CD-4 engineers superimpose the different signals on a 30,000-Hz "carrier" frequency. In effect, the rear-channel difference information rides piggyback on the high-frequency carrier, far above the audible range. That's why the cartridge must respond to such high frequencies; add 15-kHz audio to the 30-kHz carrier to get a 45-kHz overall range.

That's where the demodulator comes in. This device strips the rear-channel audio information from the high-frequency carrier, transposes it back down into the audible range, then either adds it to the already audible front-rear sum signal to get a front channel, or subtracts it from the sum to get the rear-channel signal.

Such demodulators are built into many of the latest four-channel amplifiers and receivers (and a few turntables), but "outboard" demodulators to connect between your turntable and amplifier or receiver are also widely available. In some cases, you may need special, low-capacity cables be-

Make and Model	Frequency Response Deviation in db		Recommended Tracking Force Range	Optimum Tracking Force	Trackability in cm/sec. Frequencies			Price
	Audio Range 20 Hz-20 kHz	Carrier Range 10-50 kHz			Low	Middle	High	
ADC Super XLM	±4	+0,−23	0.5—1.25	1.0	19	31.5	24	$ 75
Audio-Technica AT12S	±3	+0,−6	1.25—2.0	1.75	19	25	19	65
Audio-Technica AT15S	±2.5	+5,−4	1.5—2.0	1.6	19	20	19	100
Audio-Technica AT20SL	±3	+0,−9	1.5—2.00	1.6	24	25	19	175
Bang & Olufsen 6000	±3	+0,−20	0.7—1.5	1.2	19,	25	24	85
Empire 4000D/III	±3	+1,−6	0.25—1.25	1.2	24	31.5	24	150
Empire 4000D/I	±3	+1,−7	0.75—2.0	1.4	19	31.5	19	85
Panasonic 450C-II	(see text)	(see text)	1.5—2.5	2.3	24	31.5	19	65
Pickering UV-15/2400-Q	±3	+2,−8	1.5—2.5	2.0	19	25	19	125

Empire 4000D/I **Empire 4000d/III** **Panasonic 450C-II** **Pickering UV-15/2400-Q**

tween your turntable and demodulator to avoid carrier-frequency losses; but these are built into many modern turntables, and are often supplied with CD-4 demodulators or the components containing them.

CD-4 cartridges differ from the normal stereo models in their stylus shapes as well as in their frequency response curves. Unlike conventional stereo styli, which are either conical or oval, CD-4 styli take the shape of a three-sided, inverted pyramid with rounded edges.

Most such styli are called "Shibata" types, after their Japanese inventor, but other names (and slightly different shapes) also exist: "Pramanik," after the Bang & Olufsen stylus's designer, and "Quadrahedral" for the Pickering and Stanton design. Empire calls its version "four-dimensional."

Whatever you call it, this stylus tip is designed to present both a sharper radius (the better to trace the carrier's ultrafine groove wiggles) and a broader contact area that permits the use of higher tracking forces without increased record wear. (The reason wear doesn't increase is that a greater *force,* when spread over a broader area, results in the same *pressure*, and it's pressure, not force, that does the damage.) Of course, the tiny, pyramidal facets of the stylus tip have to be ground very precisely, and the diamond tip oriented with extreme accuracy to the stylus shank, difficult processes which largely account for these cartridges' high cost.

Our tests were run this way: First the cartridges were mounted in two new Philips 209 automatic turntables with low-capacitance cables that would not diminish the cartridges' carrier-frequency response. To obtain more precise frequency-response measurements, we used a Justi-Meter graphic recorder, then translated the curves it printed into the numerical values shown on our test chart. And we used two frequency-response test records:

a Bruel & Kjaer for the 20-20,000-Hz. audio range and JVC for the 10,000-50,000-Hz upper-frequency range.

Since all the cartridges exhibited some response out to 50,000 Hz, and since all, naturally, went out to 20 kHz, we expressed frequency response in decibels as deviations from linear ("flat") response over each of the two ranges we measured.

As might be expected, the deviations were greater in the carrier range, where any response at all is harder to achieve. Again unsurprisingly, the dips in the carrier-frequency curves were far more prominent than the frequency peaks.

But flat frequency response at carrier frequencies, while desirable, is less important than in the audio range. Low carrier output does not mean a loss of audible frequency response, but an increase in background noise when listening quadraphonically to a CD-4 disc; switch the demodulator to stereo, and the noise diminishes, while the frequency balance remains unchanged. However, once you're engrossed in the dramatic impact of the four-channel effect, the slight increase in background noise rarely interferes with your enjoyment of the music, being noticeable only in very quiet passages.

In addition to the frequency-response tests, we also conducted tests for optimum tracking force and "trackability." Both these figures will vary with the tone arm in which the cartridge is mounted—one reason manufacturers list a range of recommended tracking forces.

Contrary to common belief, the optimum tracking force is not the lowest force at which the stylus stays in the groove. Rather, it is the minimum force at which the stylus can track fairly loud signals without distortion. The lower the figure, the better the cartridge.

Trackability measures how loud a signal, in each of three frequency bands, the cartridge can trace without distortion. The louder the music, the wider the groove and the faster the stylus must move to follow it. Therefore, trackability figures are given in terms of the stylus's speed in centimeters per second (cm/sec.) as it traverses the loudest passage it can track cleanly in the low, middle and high audio ranges. We used the Shure C/PEK-3 cartridge tester and audio Obstacle Course test records to make these determinations.

tonal character is important

Technical measurements give valuable clues to a cartridge's quality, but they can't describe the tonal character it imparts to the music. The proof of this particular pudding lies in the listening. That's why we checked out each cartridge with different types of music: a symphonic score (Tchaikovsky's *Sixth Symphony,* RCA ARDI-0426), vocal music (Joni Mitchell, *Court and Spark,* Asylum EQ1001), and a brass and percussion group (Kurt Weill's *Kleine Dreigroschenmusick*, None-such H91281). After weeks of listening to test signals, this part of the test program was a pleasure. And the results showed one cartridge to be a clear standout, one below par, and the remaining seven to share a very similar—and very satisfactory—level of performance.

The standout was the B&O 6000, which played all types of music with an astounding combination of clarity and warmth of tone—two attributes rarely found together in one cartridge, but the B&O is a splendid exception. Its highs have brilliance without harshness, the bass has real depth and power without tubbiness, the strings are sweet yet transparent, the voices are natural, and the percussion has bite and impact to lift you right out of your chair. The B&O had the second sharpest drop-off in the carrier range, which our Panasonic demodulator handled with only a slight increase in noise in CD-4 playback—again not bothersome, even on CD-4 discs that had previously been played a few times by stereo cartridges. But with other demodulators, it would pay to test before buying.

At the opposite end of our subjective rating was the Panasonic. It's by no means a bad cartridge, but in comparison with the others it seemed a bit muddy, with its highs sounding choked, and its lows lacking richness. It also had the highest optimum tracking force of the nine cartridges we tested. In trackability, though, it measured better than most at low and middle frequencies, and about average at the high end. All in all, not bad

for one of the two cheapest models in our survey, even if we liked the sound of the other one (the Audio-Technica AT12S) better.

The Panasonic, unlike the others, requires a special d.c. power supply, (which is built into Panasonic and Technica demodulators). Since the Justi-Meter we used to measure frequency response has no such supply, we were unable to measure the Panasonic's response without building special adapters.

all rated well

All the other cartridges sounded remarkably good. If none quite matched the remarkable quality of the B&O, some came close—particularly the Pickering UV-15/2400-Q—and we also liked Empire's 4000D/III, which gave an exciting sense of presence to the brass. We were impressed by the smoothly balanced and eminently musical sound of both the Audio-Technica AT20SL and AT15S. In fact, we could hear no difference between the two—no great surprise, considering that the AT20SL is just an AT15S hand-picked for its performance. In our samples, this showed up in flatter carrier-range response and higher low-frequency and mid-frequency trackability.

As for the Audio-Technica AT12S, it is a real bargain, differing from the more expensive models primarily in being just a little less shiny in its uppermost highs, but still sounding sweet, rich and clear. For anyone on a budget, the AT12S would be a fine initial choice. For stereo use, the ADC would be worth the extra $10; but with the weakest carrier response of any cartridge tested, it should be checked with the demodulator you plan to use before you buy it.

All cartridges in this group are designed to work into a 100,000-ohm input, standard for all CD-4 demodulators, but not for stereo amplifiers, which normally have 47,000-ohm inputs. Since some listeners may want to use these cartridges with stereo equipment, we also tested a sampling of them by playing them through a standard stereo setup. The partial impedance mismatch seemed to have no effect, though a direct A-B comparison might have made some subtle differences audible.

To sum up: Even if you just want good stereo sound, these cartridges (and, presumably, the many new models due on the market soon) are well worth considering. And if you want to hear four-channel sound from CD-4 Quadradiscs, they're essential.

Wild new speakers—
the methods behind their madness

BY LEN FELDMAN

Here are the latest developments in speaker design. New drivers
that replace the conventional cone, new enclosures for cone speakers
and added electronics are transforming the old familiar speaker box

NEW SPEAKER DESIGNS are springing up today in as many varieties as flowers in a garden, and as fast and plentiful as weeds. Just which will bloom and which will be weeded out depends less, though, on technical ingenuity than on their sound. Many a technically plausible speaker (staid, conventional ones included) has sounded terrible, while others as ungainly and implausible as bumblebees have proven that they, like the bumblebee, can fly.

But with that warning to listen as well as look, let's survey today's new designs.

New drivers are the most obvious departure from the usual. Most unconventional is the new ESS Heil, which squeezes air out of and into its diaphragm's pleats, rather than pulling and push-

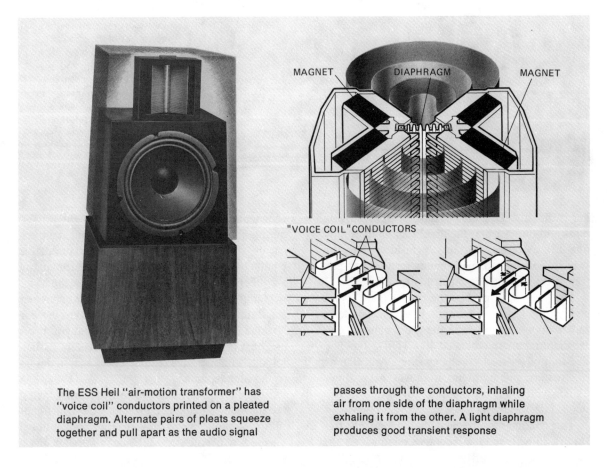

MAGNET   DIAPHRAGM   MAGNET

"VOICE COIL" CONDUCTORS

The ESS Heil "air-motion transformer" has "voice coil" conductors printed on a pleated diaphragm. Alternate pairs of pleats squeeze together and pull apart as the audio signal passes through the conductors, inhaling air from one side of the diaphragm while exhaling it from the other. A light diaphragm produces good transient response

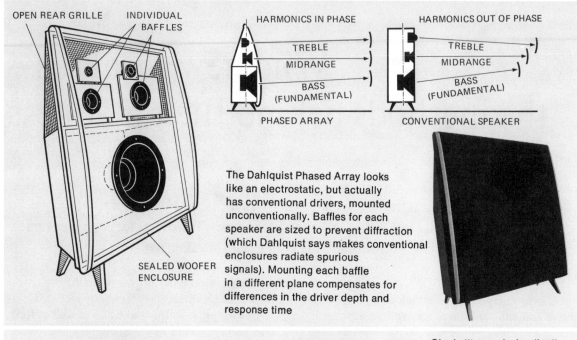

The Dahlquist Phased Array looks like an electrostatic, but actually has conventional drivers, mounted unconventionally. Baffles for each speaker are sized to prevent diffraction (which Dahlquist says makes conventional enclosures radiate spurious signals). Mounting each baffle in a different plane compensates for differences in the driver depth and response time

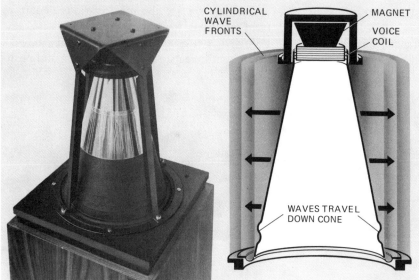

Ohm's "transmission-line" driver looks like a conventional cone driver elongated and turned inside out. Waves travel down the cone's sloping sides, radiating sound waves horizontally. Because waves take as long to travel from the perimeter of the cone's small end out to the diameter of its big end as they do to ripple down the cone's side, sound radiates in cylindrical 360° waves. Ohm makes this full-range version, while Infinity builds a tweeter version that faces up, with its large end open

ing it directly. ESS claims that its light moving mass and the fact that the diaphragm moves only one-fifth as fast as the air it's pushing gives the "air-motion transformer" better response to fast transient signals, plus much higher efficiency.

The Magneplanar, like the Heil, has its "voice coil" printed on its diaphragm in a zigzag pattern, rather than coiled around the usual round form. Its diaphragm isn't pleated like Heil's, but flat, like that of an electrostatic speaker. And like an electrostatic's diaphragm, it moves as a single plane, with good transient response due to low mass and short travel.

The conductors are heavier than an electrostatic's thin, overall conductive coating, so the

Magneplanar's transient response might not be quite a match for an electrostatic's; but the electrically simpler load imposed by the noninductive conductor layout should be easier for many amplifiers to handle. Like electrostatics, the Magneplanars beam sound fore and aft, so even small differences in the speaker's position in your room may make big differences in what you hear.

The Cerwin-Vega Magnastat tweeter, though it looks a bit like the Heil, may be closer in design to the Magneplanar.

Fisher and Polyplanar have two variations on the flat-panel speaker, both light but rigid foam-plastic diaphragms moved by conventional magnets and voice coils. Fisher's version has a specially stiffened high-frequency tweeter section driven by a second voice coil, and is available with a choice of patterns or pictures applied to the diaphragm's front surface.

The Ohm speaker may be the hardest to understand, at first, largely because it looks so much like the familiar cone speaker. But instead of pumping the air like a piston, its cone agitates the air by flexing its sides gently as sound waves ripple down its slope in rings. Sound waves move faster through the stiff cone than through air, so the ripple can move about two feet down the cone's sloping side in the time it takes the sound wave created by the ripple's beginning to travel the few inches from the cone's narrow neck out to the diameter of its wide throat—where the ripple is by then terminating. Sound therefore radiates 360° in cylindrical waves. At low frequencies, where the wavelength of the ripple would be as long as the cone's sloping side, the cone moves as a unit, radiating sound conventionally—but from what would be the back of a conventional cone. Infinity makes a tweeter speaker which works on this same "transmission-line" principle. The difference is that it is designed to face up, with its large end open.

Piezoelectric tweeters are new, even if piezoelectric devices—which convert bending stresses into electrical impulses and vice versa—have long been used in ceramic microphones, phono pickups and earphones. Different advantages are claimed by different manufacturers: Sound Technology Research claims faster, more precise response, while Poly Audio talks about virtual indestructibility, frequency response to 30 kHz, and no need for a crossover.

new cases improve the bass

New enclosure designs for conventional drivers seem mostly designed for better bass, just as new drivers seem mostly aimed at better treble. One type relies on a driver, though, a passive woofer driven not by electrical contact with the amplifier, but through its acoustical connection with the amplifier-driven (and smaller) active woofer. This "drone cone" has several benefits: it damps that woofer's motions at that speaker's resonant frequency, reducing distortion. It increases effective woofer area at low frequencies, while not adding to the relatively light main woofer's mass, so the woofer can respond with less inertia to fast transients. The drone also increases speaker efficiency by acting like a vent or port in the enclosure, while taking up far less space than an equivalently effective port would. Drones are used in the

Electro-Voice Interface:A and in various models from Polk, JBL, and Bang and Olufsen.

Another feature the Interface:A shares with other systems is an *equalizer,* an electronic network that reshapes the frequency curve of the signal fed to the speaker, first to compensate for the speaker's own diminished response at very low frequencies, and also to compensate for variations in effective bass and treble response caused by variations in the speaker's placement within the listening room. Equalized systems are also available from Audio Project, Bose, Altec, Equasound, Precision Acoustics and others and in a few compact phonograph or receiver systems.

better sound from a special port

BIC's Venturi speakers are more obviously variations on the vented enclosure. The difference here is in the snail-curved cross section of its port, designed to improve sound at all bass frequencies, not just at the frequency of the main woofer's resonance. Because your ear loses some bass and treble response at low volume levels, the Venturis also incorporate an "unequalizer" circuit that reduces low-volume mid-range till the system sounds flat to your ears again. (Your amplifier's loudness control does this, too, but only very roughly.)

The Venturi also incorporates a midrange horn of a new, compound-curved design that disperses sound over an exceptionally wide area. It covers a very broad frequency range, too (1500-15,000 Hz), to keep crossover networks and their phase distortions out of the crucial midrange—a pronounced trend in today's designs.

Unusual enclosure shapes are another route to increased dispersion. Probably the best-known of these is Bose's pentagonal 901, but there are numerous others with their speakers arrayed in pentagonal, hexagonal, triangular, spherical and vee configurations for increased dispersion, such as the Design Acoustics D-12.

Another device for increased dispersion is the rear-facing tweeter whose signals reflect from the wall, as in the E-V Interface:A and various models from Infinity, Stark and Soundcraftsmen.

the Leslie approach

Leslie's approach to better dispersion is a conventional-looking box containing an unconventional device: a rotor which constantly alters the direction in which ball waves are fed into the room. The idea is to break up "standing waves" that cause alternating areas of overrich and overlean bass within the room, and to give a livelier,

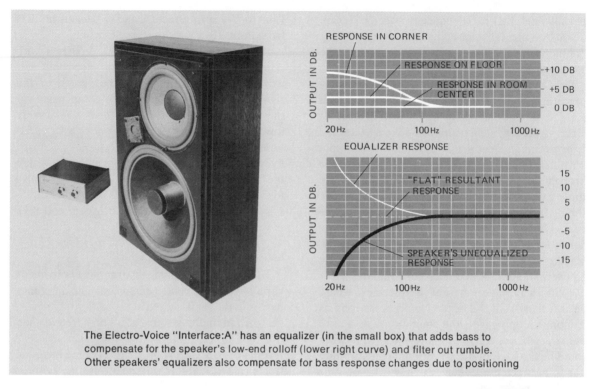

RESPONSE IN CORNER

RESPONSE ON FLOOR

RESPONSE IN ROOM CENTER

+10 DB.
+5 DB
0 DB

OUTPUT IN DB.

20 Hz   100 Hz   1000 Hz

EQUALIZER RESPONSE

"FLAT" RESULTANT RESPONSE

15
10
5
0
-5
-10
-15

OUTPUT IN DB.

SPEAKER'S UNEQUALIZED RESPONSE

20 Hz   100 Hz   1000 Hz

The Electro-Voice "Interface:A" has an equalizer (in the small box) that adds bass to compensate for the speaker's low-end rolloff (lower right curve) and filter out rumble. Other speakers' equalizers also compensate for bass response changes due to positioning

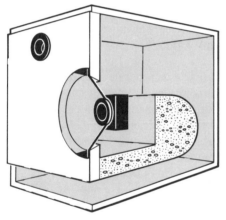

Th BIC Venturi woofer enclosure has a port that superficially resembles the bass reflex, but isn't tuned to a specific frequency as reflex ports are, so it can reinforce a broad range of bass frequencies. A built-in circuit also adds accurate loudness compensation at low volume

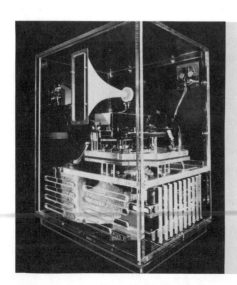

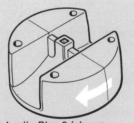

The Leslie Plus 2 (shown here in a plastic demonstration cabinet) has a revolving sound diffuser to "animate" the sound by increasing its dispersion around the room. This type of speaker is familiar to organists

The Hegeman woofer enclosure is divided into six "pipes," each a different length and resonating at a different frequency. This distributes resonance over a wide band, so the bass goes lower and is smoother than usual for such a small (26 x 11 x 8¾-inch) cabinet. A separate but coaxially mounted woofer and tweeter rest in the slanted panel at the top

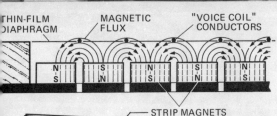

THIN-FILM DIAPHRAGM   MAGNETIC FLUX   "VOICE COIL" CONDUCTORS

STRIP MAGNETS

Magneplanar speakers look like folding screens and are just one inch thin. The "voice coil" is actually a flat zig-zag pattern of conductors on a flat diaphragm lined up opposite the gaps between strip magnets (see the cross-section plan view, above). The version shown is single-ended; a "push-pull" version with magnets on both sides of the diaphragm for minimum distortion is coming. The sound radiates from both sides of the speaker

more natural sound. The same random-phase effect is achieved electronically for the midrange and treble. In practice, the Leslie seems to work on some music, but makes other music sound a trifle "wobbly."

Servo-controlled speakers are also making news—again. The idea of turning speaker motions into a feedback signal that will reduce speaker distortion isn't new, and servo-controlled systems have been available from LWE and Infinity for some time now. With a new servo system coming from Philips (one of Europe's largest electronic firms), though, the subject will probably get a lot more discussion.

But not all of the new speaker trends are wild. One problem that has always plagued stereo buffs is the danger of "blowing out" a speaker by applying too much power. Manufacturers have now come up with a solution by building in speaker protection. The Magnum Opus and Ultralinear speakers use circuit breakers. Avid speakers use fuses, and Crown incorporates solid-state protective circuits. In this high-power-amplifier era, it's great to have this feature.

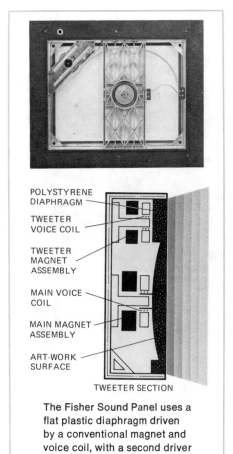

POLYSTYRENE DIAPHRAGM

TWEETER VOICE COIL

TWEETER MAGNET ASSEMBLY

MAIN VOICE COIL

MAIN MAGNET ASSEMBLY

ART-WORK SURFACE

TWEETER SECTION

The Fisher Sound Panel uses a flat plastic diaphragm driven by a conventional magnet and voice coil, with a second driver for a stiffened tweeter section. It's thin as a picture frame

The Cerwin-Vega Magnastat is similar in principle to the Magneplanar (above) with its voice coil also distributed over a thin diaphragm in a strong magnetic field, but the magnet structure is different. It's just for middle and high frequencies

The Design Acoustics D-12 is one of several systems angling several conventional drivers in various directions to disperse the sound evenly over a broad angle

Cassette decks go very posh

BY IVAN BERGER

When first introduced, cassette decks were something of a joke. But improved technology makes the newest ones sound almost as good as the reel-to-reel machines— and cost about as much, too

Peak-level indicator helps prevent distortion in recording by warning you of peak signals too short-lived to show up on slow VU meters

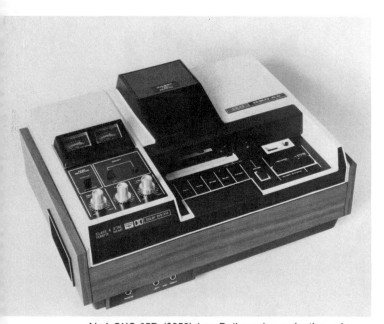

Akai GXC-65D ($350) has Dolby noise reduction, plus Akai's own Automatic Distortion Reduction System (ADRS). It flips the cassette over to play the second side

■ THE FIRST PORTABLE CASSETTE recorders made a lot of sense—but the first cassette decks designed to play through hi-fi systems seemed a joke. Hi-fi buffs could tolerate cassette performance in exchange for its obvious convenience, but could they ever respect it?

Now they can—and do. But it's taken a lot of engineering to make the cassette deck worth the high respect it now commands from the fussy hi-fi buffs.

New tapes have been a major factor in the increased popularity of cassette decks, improving the signal-to-noise ratio and distortion, while extending high-frequency response a few thousand Hz. But to make those new tapes do their best, cassette decks must allow selection of the proper high-frequency bias (fed to the record head) and

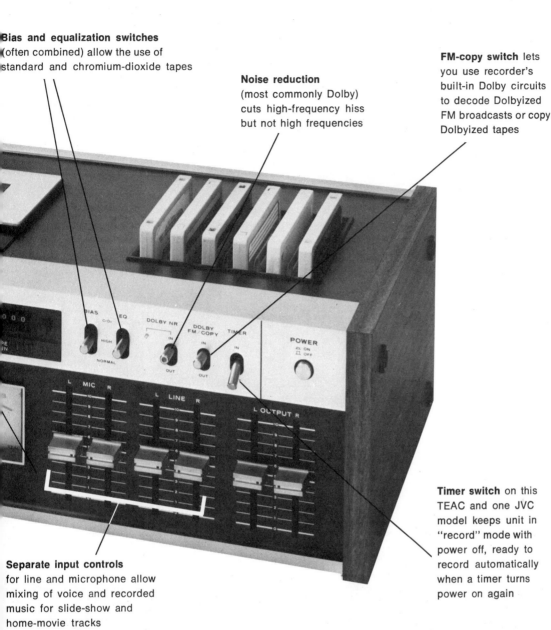

Bias and equalization switches (often combined) allow the use of standard and chromium-dioxide tapes

Noise reduction (most commonly Dolby) cuts high-frequency hiss but not high frequencies

FM-copy switch lets you use recorder's built-in Dolby circuits to decode Dolbyized FM broadcasts or copy Dolbyized tapes

Separate input controls for line and microphone allow mixing of voice and recorded music for slide-show and home-movie tracks

Timer switch on this TEAC and one JVC model keeps unit in "record" mode with power off, ready to record automatically when a timer turns power on again

the correct frequency equalization in recording and playback; most decks now do—and BASF decks do it automatically.

Noise reduction was another major advance. With cassette recordings made at one-half to one-quarter the speed of open-reel tape, and on tracks one-half to one-quarter as wide, tape hiss was a major problem. Played through wide-range stereo systems, many cassettes sounded as hissy as an orchestra of pants-pressers. The better a deck's high-frequency response, the more its hiss was audibly apparent, too.

But the Dolby system gave the cassette a valid lease on hi-fi life. Signal-to-noise ratios jumped into the 50-db to 60-db range, reducing hiss to unannoying, if not quite inaudible levels during playback.

Dolby isn't the only noise reduction system, though it's by far the commonest. JVC has its own Automatic Noise Reduction System which, like Dolby, must be used on both recording and playback (using it on only one of the two steps will alter the frequency response). It is fairly compatible with the more popular Dolby system, but not completely so.

Dolby and ANRS boost soft high-frequency tones (but not loud ones) in recording, and cut them back by an equal amount when the tape is played back. This in turn cuts back by an equal amount any noise which might have intruded during recording or playback steps. But it doesn't affect noise which might have been in the program material before it was recorded.

Philip's Dynamic Noise Limiter (DNL) system

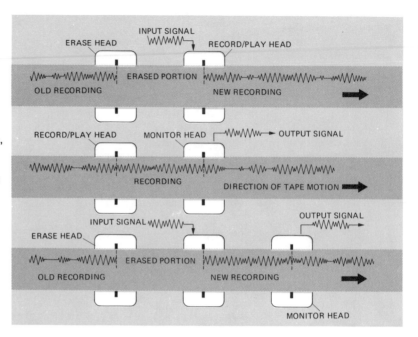

Recording and playback heads, if combined into one, require separate steps for recording (top right) and playback (right center). With a separate monitor or playback head (right), you can check recording quality by listening while recording

Monitor/play or record/play? In three-head cassette decks, the choice of which head to use for playback depends on its position. The Technics deck (below left) uses a record head, in front of the pressure pad, for highest quality playback; the third head is best used for monitoring only. Nakamichi uses its third head for monitor and playback, since it's at the pressure pad, too. (Dual capstans and pinch rollers, and a dummy head keep the tape motion smooth). Hitachi is working on a single head with separate record and play gaps

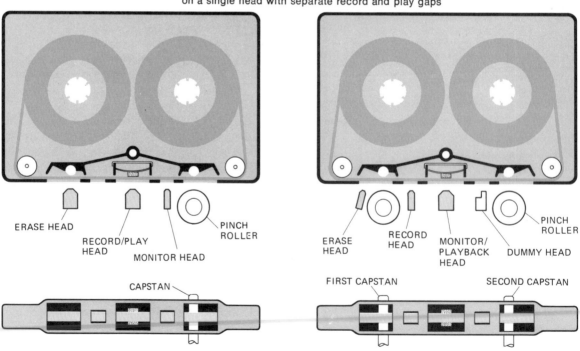

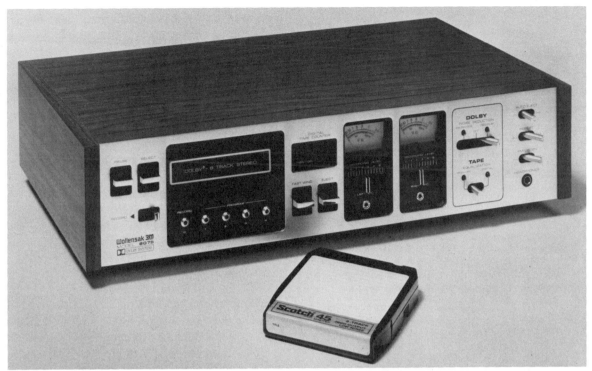

Eight-track cartridge decks are getting plushier, too; 3M's new 8075 (above) takes chromium-dioxide cartridges, has Dolby with FM switch, fast wind, auto eject and recording pause controls, plus a digital tape recorder. All controls are easily accessible on the front panel of this good-looking unit with its walnut trim

works rather differently—in playback only, sensing the high-frequency signal level. Highs weak enough to be lost in hiss anyway are cut back, but DNL lets through those strong enough to come through clearly. The only DNL-equipped recorder now sold here is the $1100 Nakamichi 1000, though DNL-equipped Philips decks are available in Canada. But the Nakamichi has both DNL and Dolby to clear up noise in the original source and limit its reoccurrence in recording.

Since Dolby's popularity is now spreading from cassette to open-reel tapes and some FM broadcasts, a few recorders now have *FM/tape copy* switches, which let you monitor through the Dolby circuit while recording already-Dolbyized material, or just use your cassette deck's Dolby circuits to de-Dolbyize such material for listening.

Distortion prevention takes an even more complex approach to noise reduction. If you try to record cassettes at levels high enough to be sure your quietest signals won't be buried in hiss, you risk the danger of overloading your tape and getting bad high-frequency distortion; both hiss and overload are more troublesome at the slower tape speeds used by cassette decks.

More "headroom" between the minimum sig-

nal that cuts through the noise and the maximum signal that won't cut your ears with distortion has been achieved by today's improved tapes, quieter recording and playback circuits, and noise reduction. That helps keep all but fast, transient peak signals from distorting.

peak-recording meters

Since those peaks can distort and disappear faster than VU meters (which read average signal levels) can detect them, more and more companies are switching to peak-reading meters or adding peak-indicating lights. Even better insurance comes from monitor-head setups that let you hear the actual recording as you make it (see diagrams, page 66). So far, only a few over-$400 machines have this handy feature.

Frequent peak-level indications tell you it's time to turn down your recording gain—but still don't warn you until a few peaks have passed. A few new machines now come with *limiters* which sense peaks and restrain them instantly. Both these limiters—unlike the automatic recording-level controls on cheaper machines—don't affect other signals. And Akai has an Automatic Distortion Reduction system that lowers high-frequency

A professional cassette deck at a professional price (about $1100) is the Nakamichi Studio A (above) with Dolby and DNL noise-reduction systems, a limiter circuit, a center-channel mike input and optional remote control

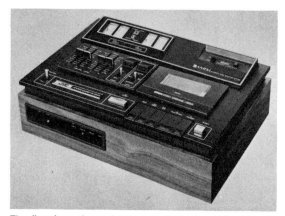

The first four-channel cassette deck, the JVC 4C01680 (above) is equipped with ANRS noise reduction system. This is similar to the Dolby approach but is not completely compatible

cassette decks, continued

gain in recording when it senses excess levels, leaving the low-level and low-frequency signals as they are received.

keeping tape speed constant

Speed control becomes more critical in a cassette deck, whose more slowly turning parts have less momentum to exert, and whose tape path lies partially inside the cassette, outside the deck designer's control. An early and still valid approach was to make rotating parts heavier, with more mass at the rim for more flywheel effect. (Some motors are even built inside-out, with outer-rotor armatures rotating around a fixed field coil.) Dual

capstans (see Nakamichi diagram, page 66) are sometimes employed to insure absolutely constant tape tension between the heads. And two other approaches—multi motor and servomotor drives—offer interesting bonuses.

Using separate motors for the capstan and the take-up and feed hubs helps keep hub-motion variations from affecting the tape speed and tension as it passes the heads. And it also results in a simpler more reliable mechanism that can be remote-controlled. Servomotors, whose speed is constantly monitored and instantaneously corrected by complicated electronic circuits, also allow slight, deliberate speed changes in playback for musical pitch control. This variable-speed feature is especially handy for a musician who is using the deck as an aid to practice.

methods of program search

Program search devices have advanced quite a bit since tape counters became nearly universal. Some counters now are connected to a memory; press a button, and the tape rewinds to whatever "zero" point you've preset. Nakamichi's more expensive deck rewinds automatically at the tape's end. Sharp now has an Automatic Program Finder, which scans for the silences between the tunes on a tape—if you don't like what you hear, you can have it automatically fast-forwarded to the start of the next tune. Both Pioneer and TEAC will soon offer fast-cue modes that let you hear the "monkey-chatter" from the tape while fast-forwarding, to help you locate the section of the tape containing the material you wish to play.

For more convenience in recording, many decks now feature bigger, easier-to-read VU meters and mixing controls that let you record from line and microphone sources simultaneously (handy for adding background music to a taped slide-show narration, for instance). Some models from Concord and Nakamichi even include three microphones: one for each channel, plus a center microphone bridged across both channels. And both TEAC and JVC have models that can be timer-controlled, to tape an FM program while you're out of the house for the evening.

cassettes are good, but have a ways to go

All of these advanced features—new tapes, noise reduction, distortion prevention, speed control and program search—have made the cassette deck a reasonable alternative for the hi-fi fan. Though they rival many open-reel decks in fidelity, they still don't quite match the best.

But they're no longer jokes—just a lot more fun.

SECTION 2

GREAT PROJECTS OF THE YEAR

On the following pages you'll find the finest of the famous Popular Mechanics *projects:*

Projects to improve your home
Projects to challenge your craftsmanship
Photo projects
Electronics know-how
Projects just for fun

You'll also find how-to information in related fields:

Shop know-how
Tool techniques
How-to tips for the great outdoors

Turn the page to find the first article on home improvement—and go on from there!

This once was a garage

BY HARRY WICKS

Imaginative use of space and materials turned this three-car garage into a charming cottage now used as a guest house

■ A LARGE PART of the fun of having a second home in the country is that you can have friends and relatives out for visits. However, extended visits often crowd the hosts as well as their guests. Weary of this inconvenience, an enterprising couple recently looked about their property on the eastern tip of Long Island to see what they could do about getting the room they often needed.

They first considered an addition to the main house. Contractor cost estimates, and the news that their year-old heating plant would have to be replaced because it could not warm additional

Before: Three-car garage offered 560 sq. ft.

After: Same building, a comfortable guest house

Wicker furniture comfortably seats six or seven without crowding the room

Kitchen-dining area. All needed appliances are in the King unit next to the half-wall

Bedroom No. 2 has ample space for two beds, roomy dresser and a nightstand

The high-riser used in the bedroom is a sofa by day, converts to a pair of beds by night

space, quickly discouraged them. Next, they looked at the usually vacant three-car garage located 150 feet from the house proper. This, they decided, would be their guest house.

Such a conversion is logical for several reasons:

1. Because the structure (shell) is already there, cost of building is sharply reduced.

2. A "guest room" set apart would assure guests and hosts complete privacy.

3. If they chose, the little house could be rented to help defray the cost.

Alterations were kept simple; no unusual or custom-built features were planned or incorporated. The biggest job on the shell was to close up the wall where the garage doors originally were located, and to install a 9-ft.-wide, sliding-door unit. The sliding-door unit selected is easy

Fitting paneling around the windows is done by holding the panel in place and marking directly from window

to assemble and install. Two men did this job in one day.

Perhaps the hardest part of the job was selecting the material to use for the interior. The small rooms demanded crisp, clean decorating which would create an illusion of spaciousness. At the same time, the man of the house wanted an in-

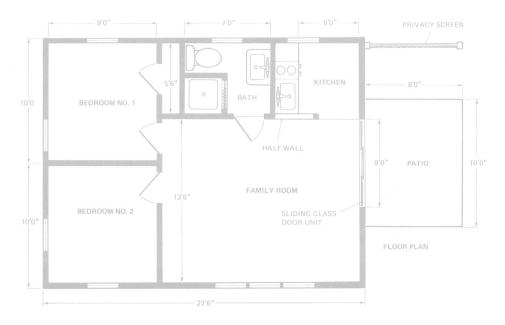

FLOOR PLAN

Window cutout in panel is made from the back side, using a circular saw. To start, use a vertical plunge

Paneling is secured in place by driving precolored nails that match the panel color

South wall of garage prior to conversion. Peachtree aluminum sliding doors were installed on this wall

Wall section comes down fast. Because wall was first framed, there is no need for a temporary support wall

Two men push frame into the opening. After plumbing frame with level, it is fastened to studs with screws

Last step is to install the door itself. Door shown is fully weatherstripped to minimize air infiltration

Triple-window mullion was installed in the wall which replaced sliding garage doors on the original front

terior that would require minimum maintenance. Both problems were solved by covering all walls and ceilings with a slightly off-white paneling, the textured look of Ranchero Nevada (by U.S. Plywood). Its finish is tough, and care consists of nothing more than an occasional wiping.

The owners felt that their guests needed a small kitchen primarily for preparing breakfast. What makes it possible to have a kitchen in such small space is the All-In-One-Kitchen Center made by the King Refrigerator Corp. In the 24x 36x39-in. cabinet there is a small sink, two cook-tops and a mini-refrigerator.

While limited space did not permit a bathtub, the $5\frac{1}{2}$x7-ft. bathroom does have a full-size shower. Also, because of its size, the house had to be carefully decorated. Old wicker furniture was resurrected, scrubbed down and painted white, and fabrics were then selected to complete the light, spacious feeling of the rooms. The attractive bedroom furniture groupings and the shutters were selected from the Montgomery Ward catalog.

Floors in the family room and bedrooms were covered with Armstrong's shag carpeting over a polyethylene vapor barrier, while kitchen and bath were treated with seamless vinyl covering.

Put an airconditioner through the wall

BY BRETT DAVID

This is a one-day job that will
let you regain full use of a window.
Furthermore, your airconditioner
is permanently installed

■ IF YOU ARE LIKE many new airconditioner owners, you've probably thought about installing your unit through a wall rather than in a window —so you'll be able to use the window. To do this, read the maker's instructions on how to 1) slide the operating unit from the outer housing (shell), and 2) remove the wingboard and side flanges that are used in routine window applications.

Begin the job outside by removing enough siding to make the cutout. To remove shingles without damaging them, slip a hacksaw blade under the shingle and cut off the nailheads. Next, slit and remove the felt to reveal the sheathing.

Using shell dimensions as a guide, outline the cutout plumb and level on the sheathing. Then

Opening is custom-cut to suit airconditioner. The unit should slide in and out easily for servicing

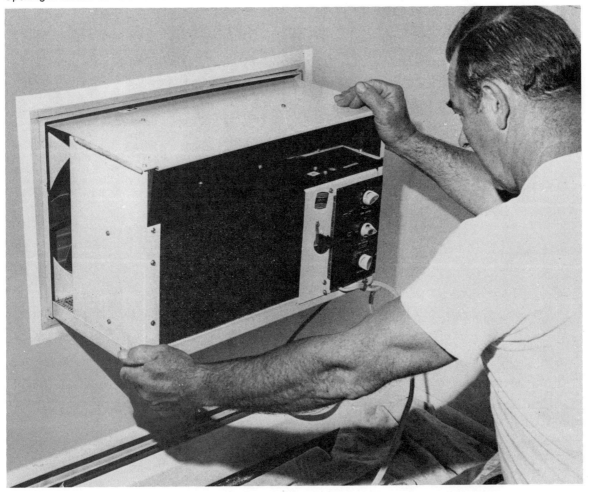

Siding (asbestos shingles, here) is removed, sheathing is cut away. If stud is in opening, it too is cut out

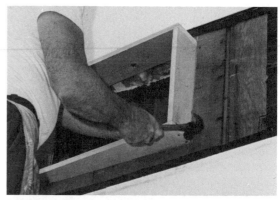

Frame is made on the ground (see drawing below for details), then set flush with sheathing at opening

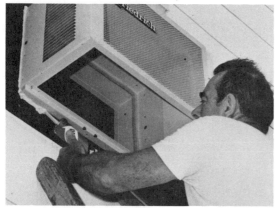

Next, airconditioner shell (exterior housing) is installed, 15-lb. felt is applied, and joints caulked

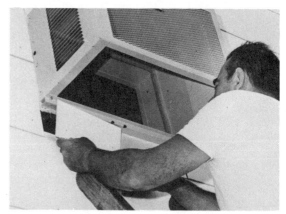

Asbestos shingles are then notched, cut and reinstalled. All of the ladder work is now completed

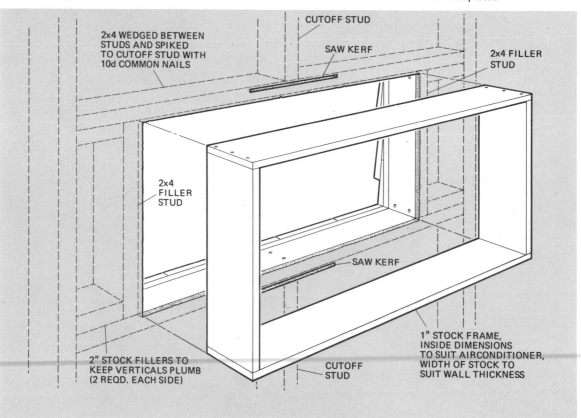

CUTOFF STUD

2x4 WEDGED BETWEEN STUDS AND SPIKED TO CUTOFF STUD WITH 10d COMMON NAILS

SAW KERF

2x4 FILLER STUD

2x4 FILLER STUD

SAW KERF

2" STOCK FILLERS TO KEEP VERTICALS PLUMB (2 REQD. EACH SIDE)

CUTOFF STUD

1" STOCK FRAME, INSIDE DIMENSIONS TO SUIT AIRCONDITIONER, WIDTH OF STOCK TO SUIT WALL THICKNESS

use a portable circular saw to cut and remove the sheathing. Using appropriate-width 1-in. (nominal) pine wood, construct the frame and build it to fit tightly around the unit's shell.

Push insulation away from the opening, remove the thin vapor barrier and then use a sabre saw to cut out studs (and plasterboard on the inside wall). Fasten the jamb in the opening, slip the outer shell into place and screw-fasten.

Outside, use a staple gun to replace the felt and seal the unit with caulk. Then cut and replace the shingles. Asbestos-cement shingles crack easily; lacking a shingle cutter, the safest way to cut them is to repeatedly score them, then snap. Use a carbide drill for nail holes.

Inside, after applying sealer tape, slide the unit into the outer shell and install the casings. Use a screwdriver to stuff insulation strip between the outer shell and the airconditioner. Finally, slip the grille in place and plug in the unit.

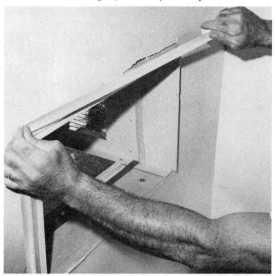

Inside, joints between new jamb and plasterboard are covered with sealing tape to keep out any drafts

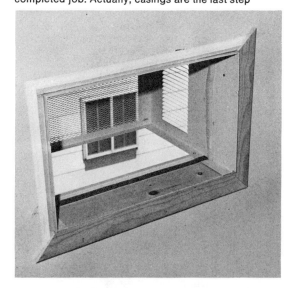

For photo purposes, airconditioner is removed to show completed job. Actually, casings are the last step

Airconditioner is slipped into opening. When it's fully seated, weatherstripping is forced into joints

Correctly installed, through-wall mount lets homeowner use window when he wants to save energy

Build a deck to gain more room

BY HARRY WICKS

One of the least expensive ways to extend your
living space is to attach a redwood deck to your house

■ FIRMLY ENTRENCHED as part of the
American lifestyle, outdoor living can be as
pleasant as you want to make it. Whether you
attach a deck to your home to serve as a transi-
tion area from house to nature, to function as a
sun trap, or to be an extension of indoor living,
it is unquestionably the least expensive way to
add living space to what you already have.

As if to prove the point that
do-it-yourself construction isn't
always as difficult as it may seem,
the deck shown above—which is
attached to a house parked on a
hilly site in San Anselmo, Calif.
—was built entirely by John Braun,
age 18. John feels the project
was worth the effort, as the
family uses it much of the time

A multilevel deck makes sense because it reduces the amount of furniture you will need when entertaining a crowd—you simply scatter pillows and use the steps. There are some basics you should be familiar with before taking on a deck project. For example, to get good appearance and high resistance to attack by insects and decay, you should consider using redwood throughout. And you can select from the lower-cost redwoods: "Construction Heart" is generally used for construction in or near the ground; "Construction Common" for decking and other off-the-ground members. Make certain you use either stainless steel, aluminum alloy or hot-dipped galvanized nails and fasteners. These won't rust and cause ugly stains on the wood. To finish the redwood, you have several choices: a clear water-repellent finish; bleach to hasten a driftwood-gray effect similar to natural weathering; or a pigmented stain which will let the grain show through

turn the page

A front view of the sturdy railing is what you see from the deck (above). Redwood planks which sandwich the rails are held together with bolts, washers and nuts. Notice that no attempt was made to conceal the boltheads. The fastening hardware has been left exposed to serve as an interesting architectural detail

This is a back view of the architectural railing surrounding the deck. Alternate posts are fashioned using three lengths of 2x6-in. material per post. The posts in between are doubled-up. Since good deck construction calls for the use of noncorrosive nails and fasteners, hefty galvanized bolts were used

A big advantage gained with a multilevel deck is that the need for a great deal of patio furniture is eliminated—you simply use the steps for extra seating. This handsome deck has levels requiring three steps and some requiring two steps as shown above

Simple, yet elegant, planters (above) are strategically located to divide the levels. These are well-stocked with plants to provide lots of color and create mood-setting decor. The potted plants rest on 2x2 rails to prevent rainwater from collecting

In the past two decades patios and terraces have evolved from little more than drab slabs of concrete to the sophisticated-looking structure shown on these pages. Of multilevel design, it has many features you may want to adopt, whether your site is hilly or flat. Of particular interest are three outstanding features: steps, planters and the railing.

The deck shown here was constructed from redwood. Redwood was chosen because it weathers well. In addition, non-rusting fasteners were used throughout to avoid ugly rust stains on the wood.

A clear water-repellent finish is highly recommended. Easy to apply, it stabilizes wood color, retards weathering and reduces moisture effects. Varnishes aren't recommended; they deteriorate rapidly in outdoor use.

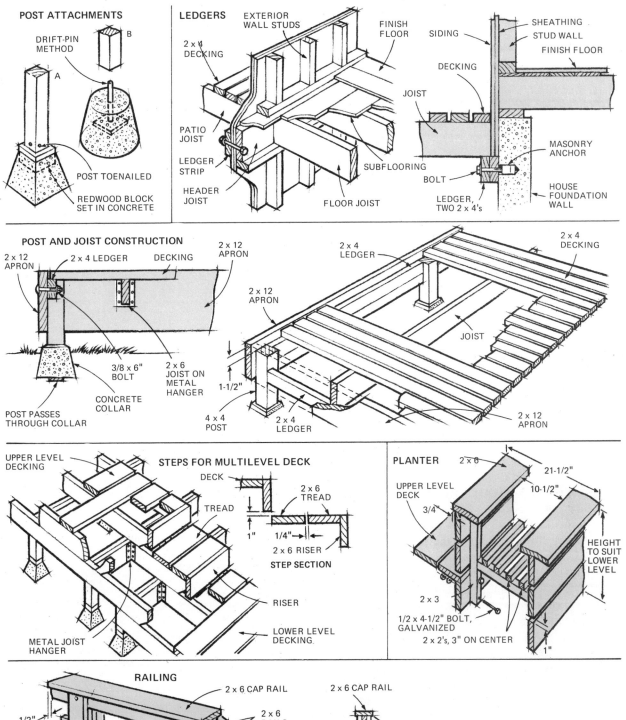

POST ATTACHMENTS

DRIFT-PIN METHOD

A

B

POST TOENAILED

REDWOOD BLOCK SET IN CONCRETE

LEDGERS

EXTERIOR WALL STUDS

2 x 4 DECKING

FINISH FLOOR

PATIO JOIST

LEDGER STRIP

HEADER JOIST

SUBFLOORING

FLOOR JOIST

SHEATHING

STUD WALL

FINISH FLOOR

SIDING

DECKING

JOIST

MASONRY ANCHOR

BOLT

LEDGER, TWO 2 x 4's

HOUSE FOUNDATION WALL

POST AND JOIST CONSTRUCTION

2 x 12 APRON

2 x 4 LEDGER

DECKING

2 x 12 APRON

3/8 x 6" BOLT

2 x 6 JOIST ON METAL HANGER

CONCRETE COLLAR

POST PASSES THROUGH COLLAR

2 x 4 LEDGER

2 x 12 APRON

2 x 4 DECKING

JOIST

1-1/2"

4 x 4 POST

2 x 4 LEDGER

2 x 12 APRON

STEPS FOR MULTILEVEL DECK

UPPER LEVEL DECKING

DECK

TREAD

2 x 6 TREAD

1"

1/4"

2 x 6 RISER

STEP SECTION

RISER

LOWER LEVEL DECKING

METAL JOIST HANGER

PLANTER

2 x 6

21-1/2"

10-1/2"

UPPER LEVEL DECK

3/4

2 x 3

1/2 x 4-1/2" BOLT, GALVANIZED

2 x 2's, 3" ON CENTER

HEIGHT TO SUIT LOWER LEVEL

1"

RAILING

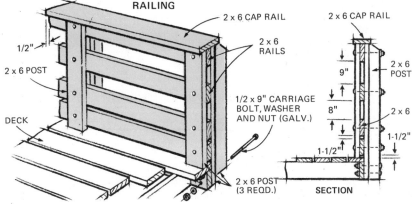

1/2"

2 x 6 POST

DECK

2 x 6 CAP RAIL

2 x 6 RAILS

1/2 x 9" CARRIAGE BOLT, WASHER AND NUT (GALV.)

2 x 6 POST (3 REQD.)

2 x 6 CAP RAIL

2 x 6 POST

9"

8"

1-1/2"

1-1/2"

2 x 6

SECTION

Clever disguises for storage buildings

Even the best sheet-metal sheds begin to get pretty beat-up after the weather takes it toll. Here are three different ways you can make them more attractive

BY WAYNE C. LECKEY

■ THERE'S GOOD REASON why outdoor lawn buildings have become so popular—homeowners have found them necessary to keep the garage from bursting at the seams. With all the yardpower equipment, the snow blower, kids' toys and bikes and a hundred and one other items that have become a part of modern living, the average garage can't house it all and the family car, too. Seeking additional room, homeowners have found lawn storage buildings the answer to the space problem.

Despite what manufacturers have done to make the buildings attractive and colorful, weathering eventually takes its toll and the sheet-metal structures begin to look a bit rundown and detract from the appearance of the property.

What can be done to make the buildings more attractive additions to a yard, even serve a greater

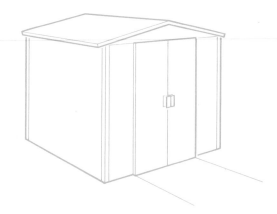

The simplest of storage buildings is the gable-roof "box." Here benches, trellises, a cupola and roof extensions disguise the shed look

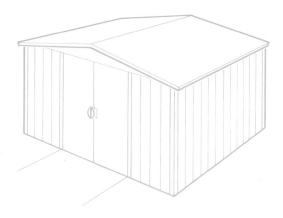

This typical unit is relieved of its plain outbuilding look by clever addition of a kid's lookout deck erected over the roof

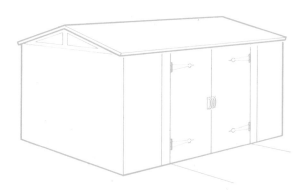

The common side-door building takes on an attractive pergola look with the addition of rafters, benches and climbing vines

82

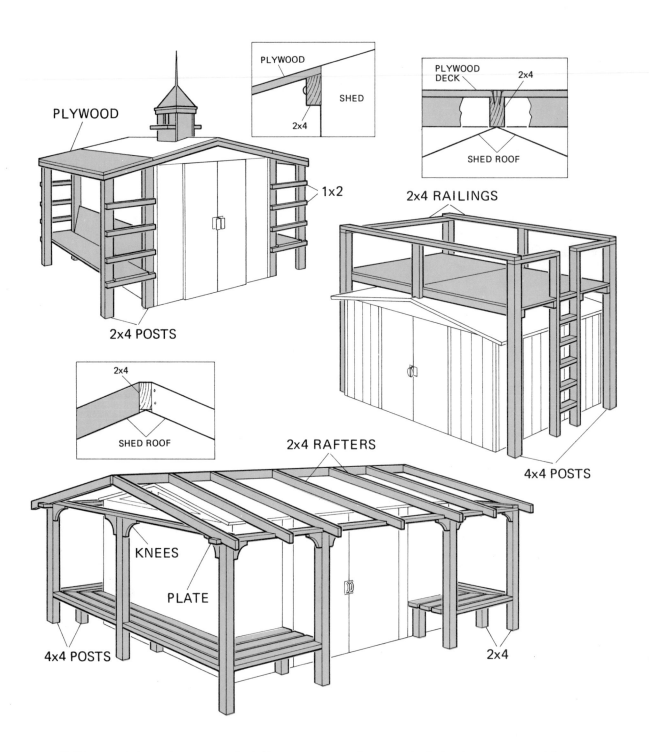

need? We tossed the assignment at Carl Sigman, a designer well known for his home face-lifting ideas, and asked that he take three of the more popular styles which are available and let us see what could be done to relieve their plain look at minimum expense.

The three designs you see here show what can be done to make such structures more attractive. One of the designs adds a pergola look, another provides a "tree house" for the kids. (For added safety, particularly for younger children, you may want to install an intermediate rail and a kickboard). All three are good examples of what a bit of face-lifting will do.

Each transformation makes use of common lumberyard members—2x4s and 4x4s, combined with sheets of exterior plywood. All members are treated with a wood preservative, and either stained or painted a matching or contrasting color.

Scrapwood makes a unique wall

Do you have a wall
that seems drab? Do you
have a lot of leftover wood
from projects? Put them together
for an exciting wall arrangement

■ WITH A LITTLE IMAGINATION, a thing of beauty can be made from the simplest, most basic materials you have around the home. And that's just what happened with the wall in this room. The idea for this textured, three-dimensional wall arrangement of wood scraps came from architect and designer Paul Albitz, who, aided by his children, finished the wall.

The first step was to frame the wall with stained 2x10s and 2x6s. All interior wood pieces are scraps of standard fir and spruce lumber, mostly 2x4 and 2x6 cutoffs left over from remodeling projects. Each piece was carefully squared, sanded and stained, and then attached to the wall with mastic cement. Result: An extremely low-cost project that is the attractive focal point of the room.

Take a look at your collection of leftover wood and adapt this basic idea to decorate a drab wall or the foyer in your home.

Grow a graceful indoor garden

■ AN INDIVIDUAL POTTED PLANT adds an attractive touch to a room. But when you group several plants in an indoor garden, you'll create a luxuriant display of foliage that hints of spring—even when snowdrifts are piled outside the window.

The arrangements shown are both practical and good-looking. They're designed to simplify daily plant care. And construction (detailed on pages 87 and 88) has been kept simple. In addition, the structures protect the floor beneath the plants.

Place your indoor garden so plants get best exposure to light. If artificial light is needed, you can use a type specially designed for horticultural purposes. (Vita-Lite by Duro-Test Corp., North Bergen, N.J. is such a light; it emits the full spectrum of natural light plus the benefits of the ultraviolet spectrum.)

Contemporary plant stand. Simplicity is the word here. The unit consists of short lengths of 2 x 10 redwood fastened to a pair of 2 x 3s. The trickiest part is maintaining the angle for the holes which receive the dowel legs. If you lack

Here are two lush indoor gardens—a contemporary plant stand (opposite page) and a living wall that blends with colonial decor (left). You can build either in just a single weekend

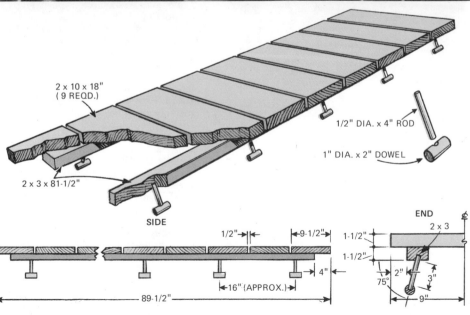

2 x 10 x 18"
(9 REQD.)

1/2" DIA. x 4" ROD

1" DIA. x 2" DOWEL

2 x 3 x 81-1/2"

SIDE

1/2"

9-1/2"

16" (APPROX.)

4"

89-1/2"

END

2 x 3

1-1/2"

1-1/2"

75°

2"

3"

9"

know-how for setting up a drilling jig, simply make the legs vertical.

Finish the stand using clear waterproof sealer on the redwood.

Living wall. Constructed of ¾-in. plywood with a 2 x 4 grid, this garden requires no elaborate joinery—all pieces are simply butt-joined.

Start by measuring the wall area and if necessary, adjust drawing dimensions. The unit's height is critical so make certain you measure carefully. The top can be flush with, or just a shade lower than, the window stool. If you build a taller unit make certain you will be able to operate the windows.

Assemble the wall unit using waterproof glue and screws since dampness is sure to get onto the wood areas. The wall unit is freestanding—unless the floor it rests on is badly out-of-level. If so, shim the unit plumb with wood shingles and use several screws through the unit's back into the wall studs. The floor grid is of 2 x 4 stock. Each well is fitted with a sheet-metal box. The joints of the box are soldered to protect the floor below.

To finish, apply a coat of primer, allow to dry and paint with colors to suit the decor of the room. For looks, paint the grid interior black and use wall color on the face to coordinate with the wall unit.

Tips for starting an indoor garden

Which plants to grow is basically a question of light source. Actually, you can grow practically any plant indoors, from roses and foliage to lush tropical varieties and cactus. It all depends on the quality of light. Do you have direct sunlight all day? Or is it partial or filtered sunlight? Or northern light? Or artificial light? Once you know the location of your indoor garden, you can select your plants using any good plant book giving a full list of light and temperature requirements.

Pots. Most indoor gardeners prefer clay pots, but you may want to pick up several ceramic jardinieres for use as color and shape accents in your planting setup.

It's a good idea to buy correct-size clay saucers to go with the pots. Pick those that have a protective coating to prevent water from seeping through to plant stand or furniture.

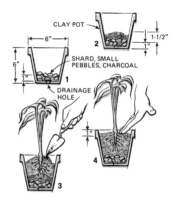

Potting a plant. Use only a clean container to pot a plant. And a new clay pot should be soaked overnight in water to minimize the amount of moisture it will draw from planting. The sketch illustrates the four basic steps of potting: 1. Fit a piece of shard (broken pot) over the drainage hole then add some porous stones. Toss in some pieces of charcoal, too, to keep the soil sweet. 2. Add a small mound of soil—about 1½ in. deep. 3. Holding the plant in place, fill around it with soil. 4. Firm the soil around the stem, then eliminate any air spaces by striking the pot on the bench several times. Soil should be about 1 in. from top so there is room for watering.

Watering and feeding. When you water, do it thoroughly—add water until excess runs from the drainage hole. Water your plants in the morning because moisture lingering at night invites fungus disease.

Humidity. Since plants release moisture through their leaves, an occasional spraying with a fine water mist is helpful.

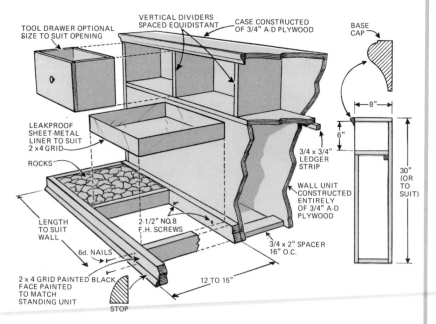

BY HARRY
WICKS

These before and after photos were taken during the first and last weeks of the same month.
Original siding was cracked and peeling. New siding looks better, reduces fuel consumption

Re-siding: you can do it yourself

■ LIKE MANY HOMEOWNERS, I simply grew tired of repainting my house every few years. That, plus the fact that I had the unrewarding experience of having paint blister, peel and scale

text continues on page 93

This homeowner and two friends re-sided an entire house in just five Saturdays. Prefinished mineral siding goes on easily, eliminates need for paint

With one side completed, the author and a friend tackle the front of the house

Mineral siding can be worked easily with tools that most do-it-yourselfers already own. The shingles come in 4-ft. lengths and are available in nine colors. Scaffolding makes the job considerably easier. On this house, gutters were torn down and replaced when siding work was completed. Left, a close-up view of the siding shows its handsome, woodlike texture, totally prefinished

Why the job was necessary

Photos of old clapboard clearly show why another paint job would no longer do much good. These before and after views indicate what a tremendous difference new siding can make. Even though the bays between the studs were vented, paint still cracked and blistered on the old siding. The last paint job was done two years before these photos were taken, and consisted of a thorough scraping and cleaning, spot-priming with aluminum paint, application of an alkyd primer, then an alkyd finish coat. Though quality paints were used throughout, the job was a failure. The only answer in such a case is application of new siding

Getting ready for the siding

First step is to remove all attachments such as shutters (left) and flowerbox beneath windows (center). The molding over the soffit-wall joint is also removed.

On this particular job it was necessary to replace the molding with a double layer of wood lath so the profile would remain unchanged

re-siding your house, continued

Applying the siding

Fifteen-lb. asphalt-saturated felt first is stapled over the existing siding. Next, wherever required for solid nailing, wood lath is nailed on below the clapboard butt edges. Corner mold then is installed at both ends of the wall run (top right). To install a corner, nails are driven through trim's flanges

into the clapboard butt edges. A double layer of wood lath then is applied to lowest clapboard (bottom left). Bottom center, backing strip is placed beneath joint of the first shingle. Bottom right, a 4-ft. level is used to level the shingle, and three nails are driven home. Chalkline could replace the level

On the first course, Kick-Strip Undercourse—a system for obtaining an architectural shadowline under butt edges—is placed on top edge of shingle before shingle goes on house (far left). To assure staggered joints, a full (48-in.) shingle is used to start the first course; half and quarter-length shingles start second and third courses respectively (near left)

Fitting siding around windows and doors

Before the shingles go on, J-channel is installed on all casings around windows and doors (see drawing, facing page). As you come to a window, hold shingle in place and mark it for cutting. Any notch size can be cut (two left photos). Door is treated in the same manner as windows (right)

Scribing inside corners

After the felt is stapled to existing siding, aluminum flashing is nailed to inside corners. This provides a valley for any rainwater that might seep through the joint. First shingle butts the corner, must be notched to fit over Kick-Strip on shingle at right. Use a metal-cutting blade in a sabre saw

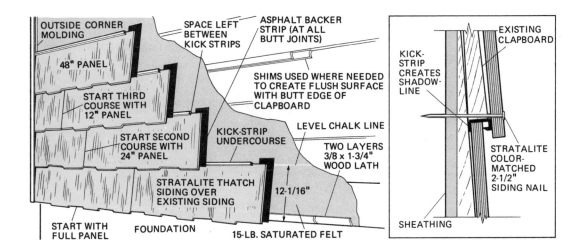

OUTSIDE CORNER MOLDING
SPACE LEFT BETWEEN KICK STRIPS
ASPHALT BACKER STRIP (AT ALL BUTT JOINTS)
48" PANEL
START THIRD COURSE WITH 12" PANEL
SHIMS USED WHERE NEEDED TO CREATE FLUSH SURFACE WITH BUTT EDGE OF CLAPBOARD
START SECOND COURSE WITH 24" PANEL
KICK-STRIP UNDERCOURSE
LEVEL CHALK LINE
TWO LAYERS 3/8 x 1-3/4" WOOD LATH
STRATALITE THATCH SIDING OVER EXISTING SIDING
12-1/16"
START WITH FULL PANEL
FOUNDATION
15-LB. SATURATED FELT

KICK-STRIP CREATES SHADOW-LINE
EXISTING CLAPBOARD
STRATALITE COLOR-MATCHED 2-1/2" SIDING NAIL
SHEATHING

J-channel is nailed to underside of the sill. The sill ends are notched to suit the vertical channels, which go up next. Use spirit level to install the channel

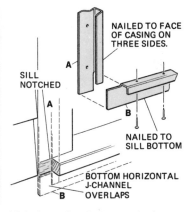

NAILED TO FACE OF CASING ON THREE SIDES.
SILL NOTCHED
A
B
NAILED TO SILL BOTTOM
BOTTOM HORIZONTAL J-CHANNEL OVERLAPS

All J-channel ends are notched; vertical (A) overlaps horizontal (B), shown by dotted lines

re-siding your house, continued

Second shingle is held in place and scribed for custom fit. To see finished corner, see photo on page 90

within two years of painting—despite the hours spent in preparation and painting and the high-quality paint used—meant this was the year for me to re-side rather than repaint.

There were several points to consider when choosing the siding:

First, I wanted my home to present a woodlike appearance that *did not* look factory-made.

Second, due to limited time and equipment, the installation procedure had to be realistically within the range of a do-it-yourselfer.

93

Working with the materials

To cut metal corner moldings and notches, use a sabre saw with a hacksaw blade

Straight cut on a shingle is made from the back side, using a carbide-tipped blade in a circular saw

re-siding your house, continued

Third, also due to limited time, the siding had to be prefinished.

I briefly entertained the notion to let someone else do it for a change, but price quotes ran from $3000 to $5000, depending on the particular siding the contractor was pushing.

So I decided to do-it-myself, selecting Strata-lite Thatch Siding S-120. Manufactured by GAF Corp., the mineral siding is available in nine colors. It comes in shingles measuring 12x48 in., and sells for $36 per square (100 sq. ft. of coverage). Color-matched installation nails and Kick-Strip undercourse (see photos, page 95) are included in the per-square price.

I measured the house for the total number of squares needed (arrived at by adding up the square footage of all walls and subtracting square footage of doors and windows) to do the job and came up with 20. I added 10 percent for waste and ordered 22 squares. Total cost of the job was $1027. Broken down, costs ran $792 for shingles, $60 for felt, staples, galvanized nails and wood lath, $75 for scaffold rental and about $100 for metal corner trim, J-channel and the like.

Even using the lowest contractor price quote which, it should be noted, called for material inferior to what I ultimately used, I saved about $1973—well worth hustling for on five or so weekends.

As can be seen in the photos and drawings, the material is easy to work with. The trickiest part of the job is applying the J-channel around windows and doors. But if a neighbor has recently had his house resided with aluminum, take a close look; most aluminum siding goes up using a similar

The finishing touch

When a shingle must be cut, a slight white crack is visible. Special touch-up paint conceals the joint

When cutting a shingle, fully support it on a plywood table. Set blade barely to clear the work

On cut or notched-on-top shingles, the Kick-Strip must be trimmed to the required length. Plastic strips cannot butt one against another because of expansion and contraction due to temperature changes. Strip is slipped on top of the shingle. On long runs it is not necessary to cut the strips. After a course of shingles is up, simply slip strips over the shingles

system. Keep in mind that the bottom horizontal goes under the sill; thus sill ends must be sawn off for the vertical channels. The dripcap at top must come off, too; J-channel replaces it. For more information and the name of the nearest Stratalite Thatch Siding dealer, write Building Products Div., Dept PM, GAF Corp., 140 West 51st St., New York, N.Y. 10020.

The special touch-up paint goes a long way; this little jar was used to touch up joints of the entire house

Paint is a perfect match for the finish on the shingles. Carry it in nail apron, paint joints as they occur

Drainage system ends flooding

A hard rain can cause
water to pour down your downspouts and
flood your foundation. This
system solves the problem by carrying
the water a safe distance from the house

■ IF YOU'RE NOT BOTHERED with water
pouring from your downspouts and flooding the
foundation of your home, you either (1) live in
a desert-like area or (2) have already provided
for underground drainage to carry roof water a
safe distance away.

Installing a downspout drainage system is a
simple job which consists of laying lengths of
3-in. perforated ABS (acrylonitrile butadiene
styrene) plastic pipe in sloping trenches 12 to 18
in. deep and tying-in the downspouts with a few
simple fittings. The far end of the underground
pipe comes to the surface (see drawing) so excess
amounts of water from a heavy downpour can
bubble up through a grating and spill out onto
the lawn. With the perforated pipe resting on a
2-in. bed of gravel or crushed stone, most of the
water from a normal rain will seep through before

How pipe joints are 'welded'

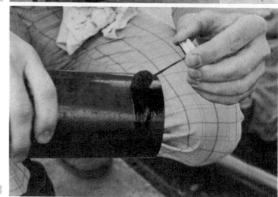

To join pipe and fittings, burrs on the ends
of the pipe are first trimmed with a sharp knife
(1). Then both pipe and fitting are wiped clean
(2). Solvent is applied to the outside of the
pipe and inside of the fitting, inserted and
given ¼ turn to spread the solvent (3)

CLOSET FLANGE AND
FLOOR-DRAIN GRATING

1/4" HOLES 4 TO 6" APART

3" NIBCO PIPE

12 TO 18"

90° ELBOW

2" GRAVEL BED

Drill drainage holes, ¼ in. in diameter, 4 in. apart in the bottom of the pipe

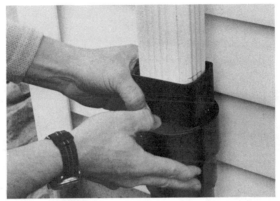

The downspout is connected to the underground pipe with a fitting that slips over its end

A Nibcoware closet flange is attached to the far end of the pipe to bring the grating flush

A round grating from a floor drain is attached to the closet flange with copper wire

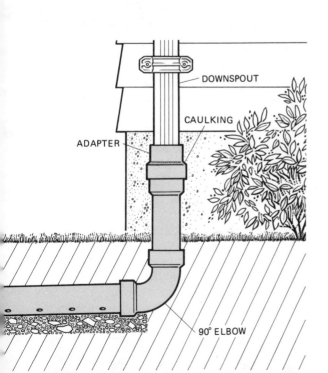

it builds up and will be absorbed by the gravel. By controlling the outflow from your downspouts in this manner, you can eliminate washouts and other damaging effects of ordinary downspout drainage.

Plastic pipe such as that made by Nibco of Elkhart, Ind., is a natural for an underground drain since it can't rust or corrode. Fittings are actually "glued" to the pipe with a cementlike substance called solvent, and the downspouts are connected with special adapter fittings which slide over the ends. Each trench is sloped a minimum of ¼ in. per foot and lined with gravel to provide a "dry well."

To prepare the pipe and fittings for gluing with solvent, first wipe each piece clean to insure a good bond. Apply the solvent to the outside of the pipe and the inside of the fitting, then press both together and give the fitting a quarter turn to spread the solvent evenly. The solvent will set almost immediately. Use the guide markings which you'll find on Nibcoware fittings to assure proper alignment.

Divide and conquer with a freestanding wall

BY HARRY WICKS

Get more from available space:
This easy-to-build wall doubles the use
of a bedroom and minimizes
disputes if two youngsters share one room

■ A PERFECT "space-doubler" for youngsters sharing the same bedroom, this freestanding wall clearly draws the line between activity and sleeping areas. Gone will be the nightly squabbles over the right time for lights out—and your role as arbiter, happily, will be vastly diminished.

Don't get discouraged about building this project because you have never built a wall before. You needn't be a master carpenter nor own any special tools to test your do-it-yourself skills on this project. The wall consists of a 2x4 framework covered on one side with plasterboard and wallpaper, and on the other side with a durable ¼-in. plywood paneling chosen from U. S. Plywood's Weldwood Prefinished line.

As in conventional house building, the easiest way to build a wall is to assemble it flat on the floor. To prevent the wall from racking (going out of square), the plywood paneling should be applied to one side while the wall is still in the horizontal position. The wall can then be tilted upright and held with diagonal braces while the plasterboard and wallpaper are applied to the second side.

There are two slight differences between this wall and the walls of your house. First, it is *not* fastened to the floor. This means that you will not be tied down to one furniture-layout scheme. Instead, a piece of ¾-in. plywood, which is attached inconspicuously to the bed frame, is in turn screw-fastened to the wall (see the inset drawing on page 100).

The second important thing to keep in mind is that the wall should stop short of ceiling height by about one foot in most homes. If it did not, the

A sophisticated, bright bedroom becomes more functional when space is divided into logical-use areas. Here, wall facing study-play area is clad with a durable prefinished plywood paneling (opposite page); the opposite side (below) is covered with plasterboard and then wallpapered to match the bedspread and draperies

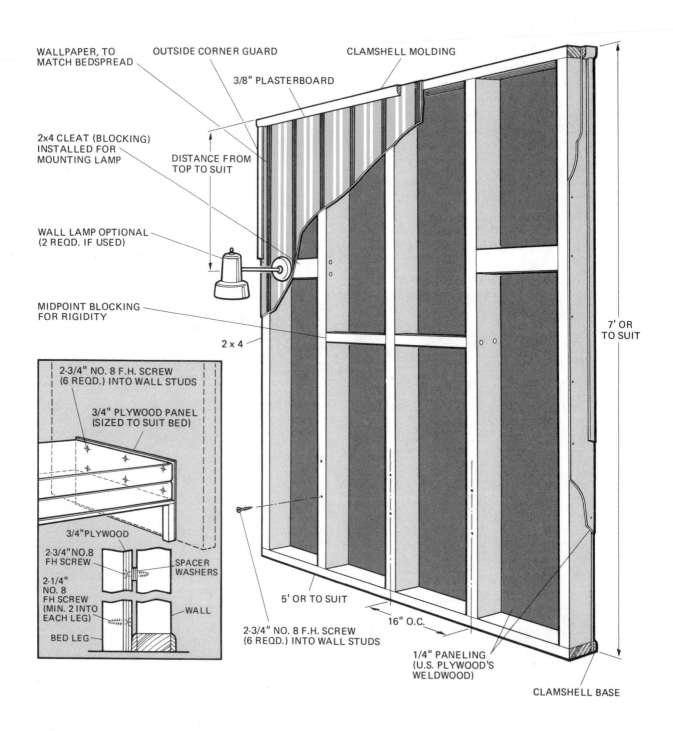

WALLPAPER, TO MATCH BEDSPREAD

OUTSIDE CORNER GUARD

CLAMSHELL MOLDING

3/8" PLASTERBOARD

2x4 CLEAT (BLOCKING) INSTALLED FOR MOUNTING LAMP

DISTANCE FROM TOP TO SUIT

WALL LAMP OPTIONAL (2 REQD. IF USED)

MIDPOINT BLOCKING FOR RIGIDITY

2 x 4

7' OR TO SUIT

2-3/4" NO. 8 F.H. SCREW (6 REQD.) INTO WALL STUDS

3/4" PLYWOOD PANEL (SIZED TO SUIT BED)

3/4" PLYWOOD

2-3/4" NO.8 FH SCREW

SPACER WASHERS

2-1/4" NO. 8 FH SCREW (MIN. 2 INTO EACH LEG)

WALL

BED LEG

5' OR TO SUIT

16" O.C.

2-3/4" NO. 8 F.H. SCREW (6 REQD.) INTO WALL STUDS

1/4" PANELING (U.S. PLYWOOD'S WELDWOOD)

CLAMSHELL BASE

resulting look would be wall rather than divider. Before starting construction, make certain you measure bedroom floor-to-ceiling height and scale your divider to it (as well as scaling the divider width to bed width).

The wall facing the active area is most likely to receive some punishment from lively youngsters. Thus, it is clad with the same plywood paneling used on the bedroom walls. Paneling here also gives a feeling of continuity—that the

wall is an integral part of the room. Lacking such coordination, it might look like an afterthought.

The second side is covered with ⅜-in. plasterboard. Joints and dimpled nailheads are hidden with two applications of joint compound and the wall is finished with wallpaper to match bedspread and draperies. Conventional molding at top, base and corners supply the finishing touches. If desired, battery-powered pin-up lamps can be installed on the divider over the bed.

Sewing built-ins

■ SINCE MENDING is often done in connection with washing clothes, a logical place for a sewing built-in is the laundry room. Complete with portable machine and a pegboard wall to hold patterns and sewing essentials, plus a clock and phone, the built-in sewing nook at left is an idea from Maytag that makes good sense.

Three flush doors supported by four two-drawer file cabinets placed along a wall make a complete sewing center (below, right). The file cabinets provide eight roomy storage drawers for yard goods and patterns galore, and the long counter gives all the room in the world to lay out and cut a pattern.

An unusual way to find space for a convenient sewing center is in a spare bedroom closet (below). Folding doors cover the opening when you close up shop for the day.

Built-in next to the washer and the clothes bin, this tidy sewing center is handy for sewing a rip in Junior's jeans. After the mending is complete the washing machine is right there to throw the dirty clothes in. Behind the machine is a pegboard wall to hold scissors and other sewing essentials

A quickie to rig is this "built-in." The counter is made of three flush doors and is supported by common metal file cabinets. Kneeholes and chairs provide comfort at each of the sewing stations

This sewing built-in was once a spare bedroom closet. The machine counter should be 30 in. high to provide a kneehole. The shelves in the back hold sewing supplies. The folding doors close to hide everything

New look for a tired wall

To cover some unsightly cracks and sagging ceiling joists, this homeowner built a fin-type 'living' wall unit which is visually held together by the use of a dropped soffit

■ SETTLING CAUSED the outside wall to crack and the ceiling joists to sag in one of the upstair's bedrooms of James Cherry's 80-year-old house in Minneapolis. While repairing the wall, Mr. Cherry got the idea to convert the seldom-used guest room into a den-sitting-room-library where he could relax, read and listen to music.

Because the room is large with a high ceiling,

the owner wanted to create a feeling of intimacy. After considering the options, he achieved this effect by filling the window wall from floor to ceiling and corner to corner with the bookshelf system shown on these pages. Visually, the change reduces the room in size; practically, it hides the cracked wall and gives support to those sagging ceiling joists.

The wall system designed by Mr. Cherry is based on plasterboard-covered 2x4 frames with shelving in between. For visual uniformity, the dropped soffit was built-in. The design can easily be adapted to any size wall with a little careful planning. Desk-level and floor-level shelves project slightly more than bookshelves to lessen the dominance of the vertical fins.

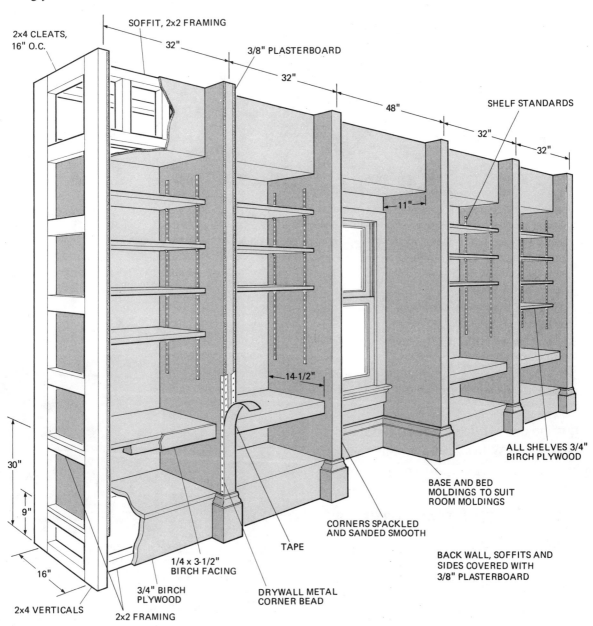

2x4 CLEATS, 16" O.C.

SOFFIT, 2x2 FRAMING

32"

3/8" PLASTERBOARD

32"

48"

SHELF STANDARDS

32"

32"

11"

14-1/2"

30"

9"

16"

2x4 VERTICALS

2x2 FRAMING

3/4" BIRCH PLYWOOD

1/4 x 3-1/2" BIRCH FACING

DRYWALL METAL CORNER BEAD

TAPE

CORNERS SPACKLED AND SANDED SMOOTH

ALL SHELVES 3/4" BIRCH PLYWOOD

BASE AND BED MOLDINGS TO SUIT ROOM MOLDINGS

BACK WALL, SOFFITS AND SIDES COVERED WITH 3/8" PLASTERBOARD

An unused bedroom was converted to the combination den-sitting-room-library at the left
This sturdy wall unit, with several shelves for books and speakers, four desk-level shelves
for lamp and decorations, and four floor-level shelves for stereo receiver and more books,
makes the room feel more intimate, while supporting sagging ceiling joists

This view, taken from the same point as the photo below, was taken after remodeling. Rich walnut paneling was installed over furring strips nailed to the old wall. The handsome library wall features recessed lighting

Basement remodeling ideas

A family room doesn't have to look as if it's in a basement. With a little imagination you can give it a living-room warmth

■ THE DRAMATIC TRANSFORMATION of a family room shown on these pages is the work of interior designer Virginia Frankel, AID. Her client, a resident of Long Island, is a collector of rare books and lithographs. He wanted the room renovated to fulfill several specific needs. First, it had to house his rare-book collection. Second, he wanted to use it occasionally as a home office.

This is the view that greeted Ms Frankel when she arrived. Note the almost-useless window and wood paneling installed halfway up the wall, which magnifies, rather than camouflages, the foundation wall in this split-level basement

And, if needed, it had to be able to do double duty as a guest room.

The family room was dramatically changed from uninteresting to elegant and vibrant mainly by using rich, luxurious walnut paneling from U. S. Plywood's Weldwood collection. Ms Frankel was so successful in her efforts that the owners now confess to "almost full-time living in the room."

The conspicuous foundation-wall ledge typical of split-levels, was hidden by paneling fastened to furring strips installed over the existing wall. Cleverly arranged cafe curtains and drapes are used to hide the ledge behind the sleep-in sofa shown below.

The almost-useless window to the left of the triple mullion was closed in and concealed by installing bookshelves over the ledge; cabinets below this bookcase are fake. They are intended to carry out the library wall theme. The finished room suits this family's needs perfectly. More important, there are many features shown here that could be incorporated into the family room in almost any house.

These before and after pictures show what was done with the offcenter triple-mullion and half-wood wall. Creative use of paneling, a cafe-curtain arrangement and fake cabinets under the bookshelves mask the foundation ledge which had been obvious. Window shades are covered to match the curtains

THERE ARE THREE basic points to keep in mind when you install kitchen cabinets: 1. Base cabinets must be set level, thus shims are usually required. 2. Cabinets must be securely fastened to wall studs. Although many contractors install cabinets using hefty (16d) common nails, proper-size wood screws are a better choice. 3. You must stick to the architectural kitchen standards shown in the drawing at left, below. These dimensions are important; any variance from standard working and reaching heights and depths will result in an uncomfortable-to-work-in kitchen. Also, keep in mind that kitchen cabinets are, in fact, pieces of fine furniture; handle with care to avoid scratching or marring the finish. And keep tools off the countertop.

How to install kitchen cabinets

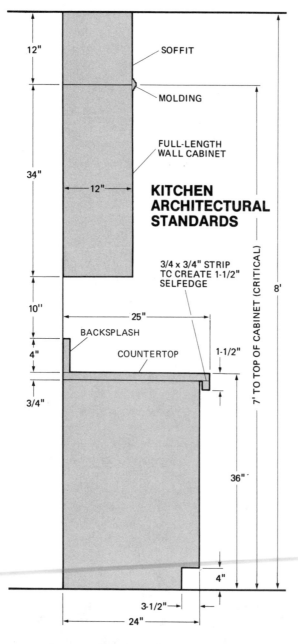

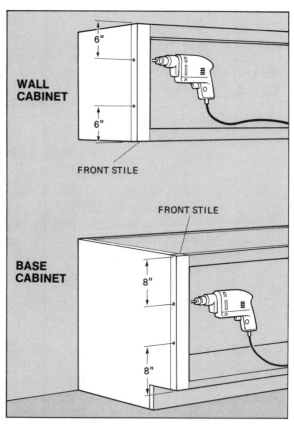

Joining two cabinets

Start by drilling installation holes in stiles of those cabinets that will butt another. Holes should be large enough for fastening screws to slide freely. Butt the two cabinets and, using each installation hole as a guide, drill a smaller, correct-size pilot hole in the adjacent cabinet's stile. Later, as screws are turned home, they will take their bite in the adjacent stile and pull the joint tightly closed. Hole locations are shown above; for less than full (34 in. high) hangers, usually only one hole is needed at the stile center. Use additional screws wherever the joint is not tight

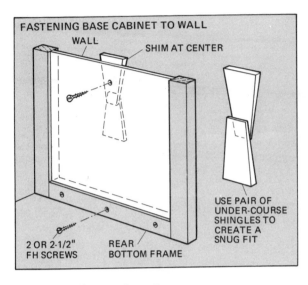

FASTENING BASE CABINET TO WALL

WALL
SHIM AT CENTER
2 OR 2-1/2" FH SCREWS
REAR BOTTOM FRAME
USE PAIR OF UNDER-COURSE SHINGLES TO CREATE A SNUG FIT

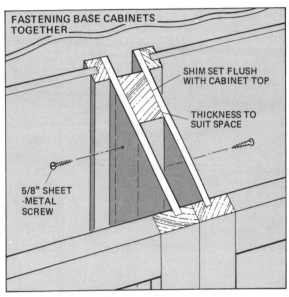

FASTENING BASE CABINETS TOGETHER

SHIM SET FLUSH WITH CABINET TOP
THICKNESS TO SUIT SPACE
5/8" SHEET-METAL SCREW

Fastening cabinets to the wall

If it is necessary to drive screws through the back plywood panel to penetrate a wall stud when attaching a base cabinet (above), use shims—undercourse shingles—to assure a rigid installation and to prevent bowing the cabinet's back. Use this method on base cabinets only. For wall cabinets, install 2-in. No. 10 wood screws through the wood fastening rail at the inside top back of the cabinet

Shimming between cabinets

If stiles project beyond sides, use a shim between cabinets as shown. The shim can be of solid wood if the dimension matches stock lumber. For example, if the space between is ¾ in., simply use ¾-in. pine or plywood. For odd dimensions, use a pair of shingles (as shown above, left) to obtain a good snug fit

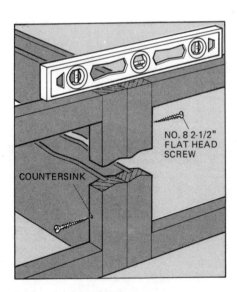

NO. 8 2-1/2" FLAT HEAD SCREW
COUNTERSINK

Joining front frames

Use your spirit level (a 4-footer is best) to level cabinets. Where necessary, slip a shim under a low cabinet to bring it up into the same plane as the fastened first cabinet. When satisfied with alignment and plumb, join the cabinets by installing 2½-in. screws through the installation holes you drilled earlier. Use flathead screws and countersink them so operation of doors, drawers will be smooth

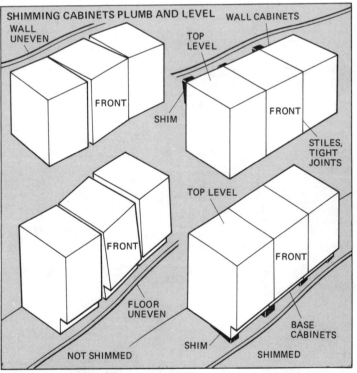

SHIMMING CABINETS PLUMB AND LEVEL

WALL CABINETS
WALL UNEVEN
FRONT
TOP LEVEL
SHIM
FRONT
STILES, TIGHT JOINTS
FRONT
TOP LEVEL
FLOOR UNEVEN
FRONT
NOT SHIMMED
SHIM
SHIMMED
BASE CABINETS

Floor and wall shimming

If your floors and walls are not level and plumb, it is a must to shim behind the base and wall cabinets to the highest point as is shown above. Shimming assures proper alignment of horizontal cabinet rails for appearance, and is necessary to assure that the doors and drawers will function properly after installation

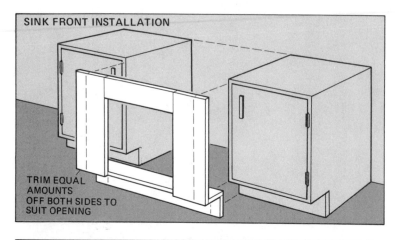

SINK FRONT INSTALLATION

TRIM EQUAL AMOUNTS OFF BOTH SIDES TO SUIT OPENING

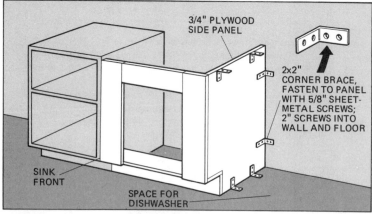

3/4" PLYWOOD SIDE PANEL

2x2" CORNER BRACE, FASTEN TO PANEL WITH 5/8" SHEET-METAL SCREWS; 2" SCREWS INTO WALL AND FLOOR

SINK FRONT

SPACE FOR DISHWASHER

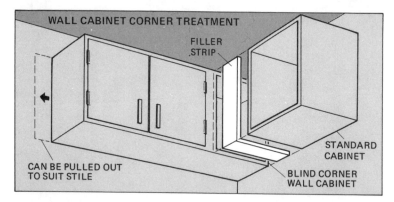

WALL CABINET CORNER TREATMENT

FILLER STRIP

CAN BE PULLED OUT TO SUIT STILE

STANDARD CABINET

BLIND CORNER WALL CABINET

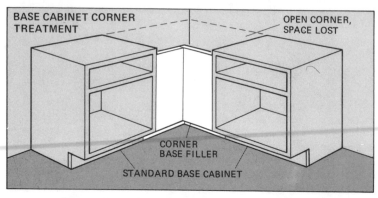

BASE CABINET CORNER TREATMENT

OPEN CORNER, SPACE LOST

CORNER BASE FILLER

STANDARD BASE CABINET

Sink-front installation

Generally a sink front (designated (SF), not a cabinet, is used below a kitchen sink. Since the most widely used single sink is 24 in. wide and 21 in. deep, most sink fronts come in 24-in. widths. Larger widths for oversize and double sinks are also manufactured. Some makers put extra-wide stiles on the SF so that they can be trimmed to the required size (width) on the job. Sink fronts are secured by fastening through stiles to the side cabinets

Dishwasher next to sink front

If your layout calls for a dishwasher (DW) to be located next to the sink, an extra step will be necessary. Since there is no cabinet for fastening SF on DW side, it is necessary to cut a ¾-in. plywood panel to serve as a sidewall. For rigidity, fasten the plywood "side" to the floor and wall using 2x2-in. corner braces. After countertop is installed, add corner braces from plywood panel to underside of countertop; use ⅝-in. sheet-metal screws to top

Blind corner wall cabinet

Installation is the same as for other wall-hung cabinets except that a 3-in. filler is used between the blind cabinet and the cabinet butting it at 90° (to assure clearance for door swing). The filler is attached by screws through the hanger cabinet, and from inside the blind corner hanger into the filler. Butting cabinets are hung conventionally using screws through the inside back top rail into the wall studs

Corner base filler

Base cabinets can be installed as shown at left by using a corner base filler. Though there is a cash saving initially when this type corner is used, it is recommended only for kitchens with ample space. Once closed in, that corner area is space lost for good. To utilize corner space, consider instead installing a blind corner cabinet (BCC). For a drawing of a BCC look at the top of the next page on the left

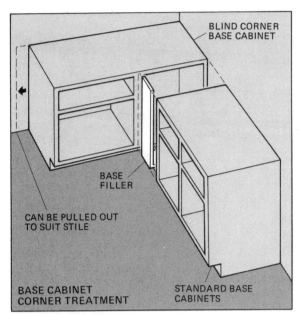

Blind corner base cabinet

A standard cabinet is installed with filler between it and the blind corner base cabinet (BCC). Fasten the filler with screws through standard cabinet's stile and if possible, with screws through BCC center stile into opposite edge of the filler. Access to corner space is through the standard-cabinet door

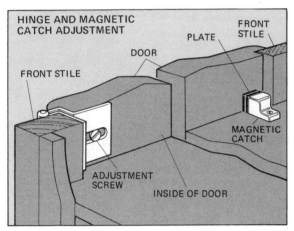

Adjusting doors

Since misalignment of doors and drawers can be caused by rough handling during shipment, most of the manufacturers pack door and drawer adjustment right in with the cabinets. Realignment of these parts generally consists of simply loosening the hinge screws slightly, squaring the doors and retightening the screws. It is also frequently necessary to adjust a magnetic catch; you simply loosen the screws and slide the magnet forward or backward in its slots until the desired contact action has been accomplished. Then retighten the screws

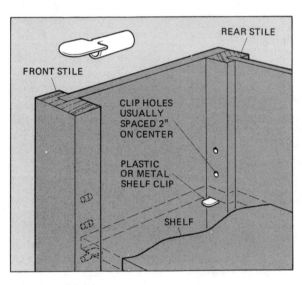

Shelf installation

Most base cabinets come with a fixed shelf; full-height wall cabinets usually contain two adjustable shelves. Though there are several kinds of adjustable shelving systems, a commonly used type consists of plastic or metal supports pushed into predrilled holes in wall-cabinet stiles. Simply insert four supports for each shelf and lay it in place. If the shelf rocks, firmly "slap" it in the middle to true up supports and seat the shelf squarely

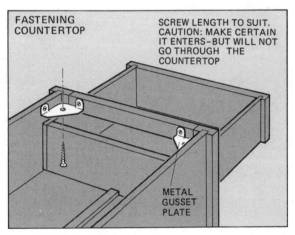

Installing the countertop

Usually, base cabinets have metal gusset plates in each corner at the top. These serve a dual purpose: Adding strength to the cabinet and anchoring the countertop. With the countertop in position, carefully measure the length of screw required to obtain a purchase in top's underside without coming through the laminate finish. Not many screws are required here as their primary function is simply to keep the top from shifting laterally

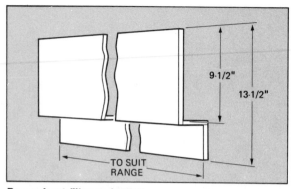

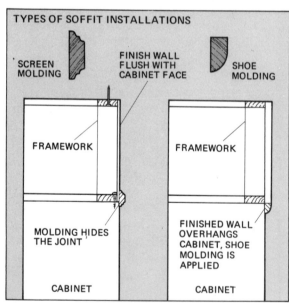

SOFFIT FRAMEWORK OF 1x3 STOCK

6d COMMON NAILS

Range front filler and panel

The range front filler and panel are used when a drop-in range/oven is to be installed. Some ranges call for more elaborate filler pieces than others; thus the range should be picked before the cabinets are ordered and the maker's specifications checked to see if—and what type of—a wood front is needed. A specified size of ¼-in. paneling, finished to match the cabinets, may be all that's required. Bring these specs along when you order the cabinets

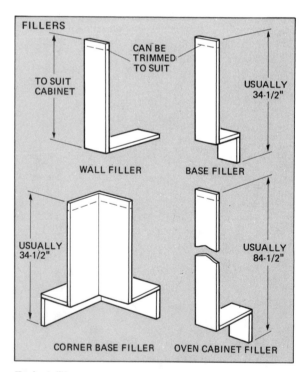

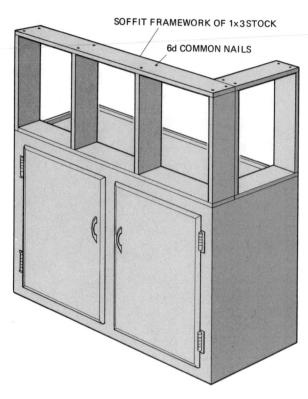

Typical fillers

The most commonly used fillers are shown above. Besides serving for blind corner-cabinet installation, these are required when a cabinet run will butt a wall at 90°, and when a wall is so out of plumb or irregular that it will be necessary to scribe (custom-fit) the last cabinet to the wall

Installing the soffit

The easiest-to-make soffit enclosure is a ladderlike structure made of 1x3 furring. Take accurate measurements between the cabinet and the ceiling at ends and middle of run and assemble sections on the floor. Then hoist the sections in place and fasten using shims as needed. Framework can be set back a distance equal to thickness of material covering it, or installed flush with the cabinet fronts

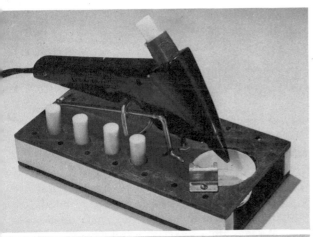

Caddy
for your glue gun

BY CHARLES GREEN

■ IF YOU HAVE USED an electric glue gun, I'm sure you have been puzzled each time with where to rest it and how to keep the drips which ooze from the tip from messing up your bench. I solved those problems by making this holder. It lets me park my gun safely while hot, catch the drips from the tip, scrape off the leftovers to keep the tip clean and store a supply of glue-stick refills.

The drawing shows how it's made. The gun's cradle is a modified standard hook used with perforated hardboard. It's mounted upside down in the holes and wired in place. A second hook, bent as shown, plus an adjustable stovebolt, supports the gun so its tip is centered over the disposable paper cup.

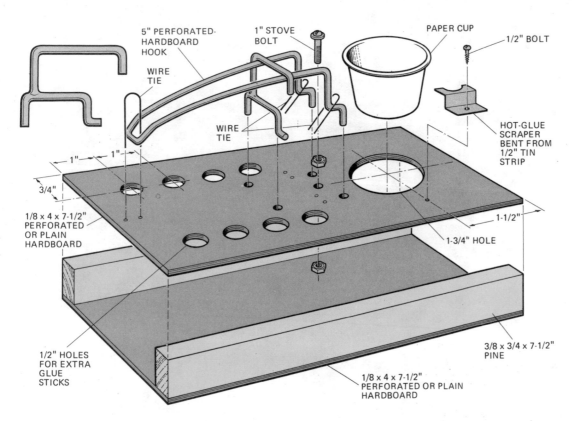

5" PERFORATED-HARDBOARD HOOK

1" STOVE BOLT

PAPER CUP

1/2" BOLT

WIRE TIE

WIRE TIE

HOT-GLUE SCRAPER BENT FROM 1/2" TIN STRIP

1"

1"

3/4"

1/8 x 4 x 7-1/2" PERFORATED OR PLAIN HARDBOARD

1-1/2"

1-3/4" HOLE

1/2" HOLES FOR EXTRA GLUE STICKS

3/8 x 3/4 x 7-1/2" PINE

1/8 x 4 x 7-1/2" PERFORATED OR PLAIN HARDBOARD

Use the right saw blade

■ WHEN ONE TYPE of saw blade is used to cut all kinds of material, it's almost like using one size nail to build a house. Only when a plywood blade is used to cut plywood, or a hardboard blade is used to cut hardboard, for example, can you turn out the best work and get the most from your bench saw or portable power saw.

That's why a selection of blades having a wide range of tooth patterns is available, each de-

signed to cut a specific material in the best, fastest and smoothest way.

For general-purpose cutting, both with and across grain, a flat combination blade is your best bet, but, again, it won't match the extra-smooth cut you get with a hollow-ground planer blade. Thus it's important to keep several types of saw blades on hand so you can switch from one to the other, whatever your cutting requirements.

Carbide-tip blade

**Combination blade
(hollow ground)**

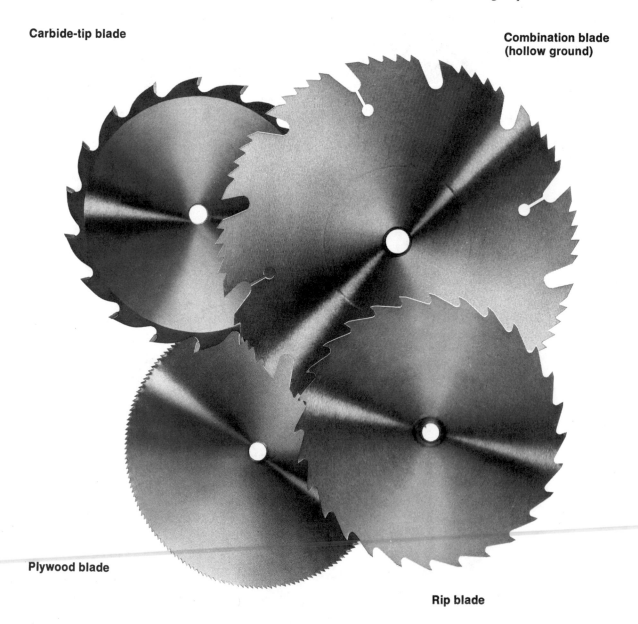

Plywood blade

Rip blade

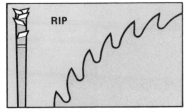

RIP

For ripping all hardwoods and softwoods. Has heavy hub, is taper-ground for extra clearance

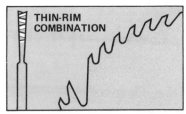

THIN-RIM COMBINATION

Finest combination blade for fine trim and finish work. Use it to rip, crosscut or miter

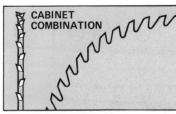

CABINET COMBINATION

Cabinetmaker's combination blade cuts in any direction through either hardwoods or softwoods

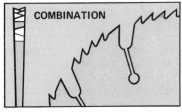

COMBINATION

Cabinetmaker's blade. Produces smooth and accurate cuts in any direction in hardwoods

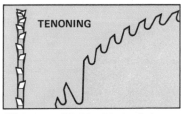

TENONING

All-purpose blade, wide-kerfed for cutting tenons, splines in all hardwoods and softwoods

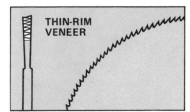

THIN-RIM VENEER

For satin-smooth finish cuts in either plywood or thin veneers without splintering

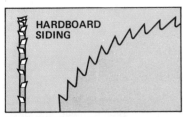

HARDBOARD SIDING

Best blade for cutting tempered hardboard underlayment, siding, perforated board

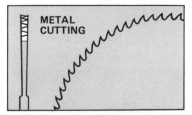

METAL CUTTING

Intended for aluminum, brass, bronze, copper, zinc and lead. A truly professional blade

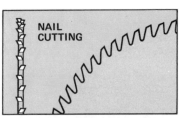

NAIL CUTTING

For rough-cutting (rip and crosscut) through all woods that have an occasional nail

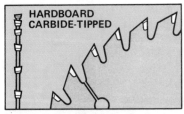

HARDBOARD CARBIDE-TIPPED

Excellent for wood, but can also be used on hardboard siding. Its 32 teeth cut fast, straight

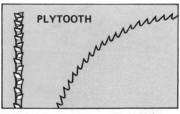

PLYTOOTH

Fine-tooth, smooth-cutting blade for plywood, composition board, soft board and the like

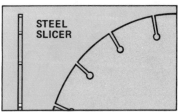

STEEL SLICER

For light-gauge sheet steel, roofing, guttering and downspouts, up to 1/16-in. thick

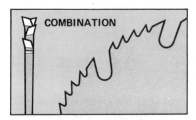

COMBINATION

Good for ripping, crosscutting, mitering on all hardwoods and softwoods. Comes taper-ground

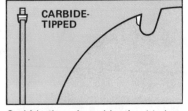

CARBIDE-TIPPED

Carbide-tipped combination blade for long cutting life; ideal for abrasive materials

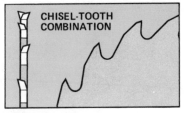

CHISEL-TOOTH COMBINATION

All-purpose, fast-cutting blade for all woods. An excellent contractor's framing blade

How to paint with spray cans

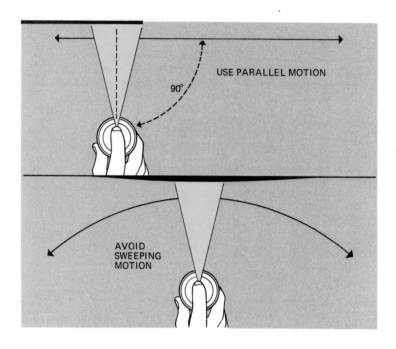

There's a knack to it

While the pressurized spray can has made painting a lot simpler than it used to be, there's a knack to handling these self-contained spray guns beyond just pressing a button. One of the secrets of a perfect paint job is to keep the can moving at all times. Another thing to remember is that the paint goes on in a uniform layer when the distance between the spray head and the surface is the same throughout a parallel sweep, as shown in the upper diagram, on the left. When applied with a sweeping motion as shown in the lower diagram, the paint film is heavy at the center of the arc and thin at each end, producing a coating which is not uniform

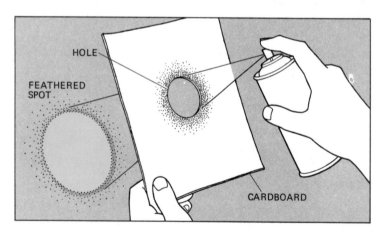

Feathering is a touch-up trick

A neat trick to remember when doing touch-up work, such as refinishing a fender scratch, is to aim the nozzle through a hole in a piece of cardboard held 10 in. or so from the surface. This feathers the edges so the paint will blend into the surrounding area rather than concentrate in a single spot

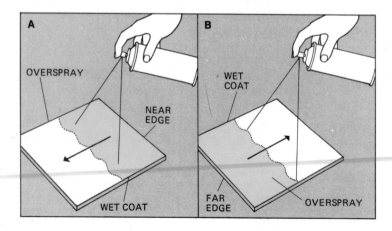

Always work from the near edge

When painting a horizontal surface such as the top of a table, start at the near edge and work away (A). This lets the overspray (mist) settle ahead of the full wet coat following. Working from the far edge (B) allows the mist to fall on top of the wet coat, producing a less smooth, "pitted" finish. Several thin coats will produce better coverage and hiding quality than one thick coat. Since aerosol paints are generally quick-drying, succeeding coats can be applied as litle as five minutes apart

Wait until paint is warm

To dry properly, paint in aerosol cans should be at a temperature between 60° and 90° F. If cans are stored in a garage or other unheated place during cold weather, the paint will be too cold to use immediately. To warm it, place the can in a pan of lukewarm water (*not* over a fire) for a few minutes

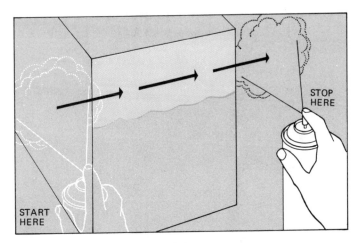

Start spraying before you paint

When spraying flat vertical surfaces, learn to trigger the spray so you start and stop the spray stroke off the work. This results in an even coating. Stay parallel to the surface and move back and forth across the full width of the work with each pass. Hold the spray head 10 to 12 in. from the surface and use a firmly rapid stroke. If applied too slowly, the spray concentration becomes too great and the paint will run and sag on vertical surfaces. Shake the can to keep the paint well mixed

Good to the last drop

When a can is nearly empty and fails to spray when it's tilted, chances are that the siphon tube is above the paint level as shown in cutaway A. The remaining contents can be reached in most cases by turning the spray head 180° or until the siphon tube is in the lowest part of the can and below the paint level, as in B

Keep it clean when job is done

After each job, be sure to clear the spray head of the paint so it won't be clogged for the next use. To do so, turn the can upside down and give the spray a few bursts to blow out the pinhole orifice. Aim the nozzle at a dropcloth or newspaper as some remnants of paint will be forced out along with the gas. Even when emptied of paint, enough pressure is left to be a hazard. Before disposing of any aerosol can, hold down the spray head (release valve) until the remaining gas is completely exhausted

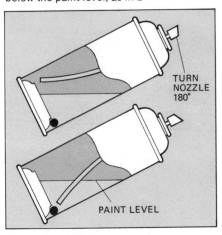

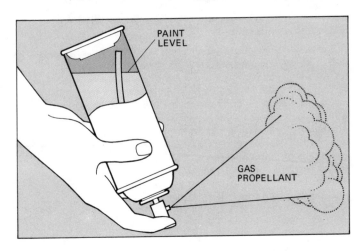

16 ways to hide plywood edges

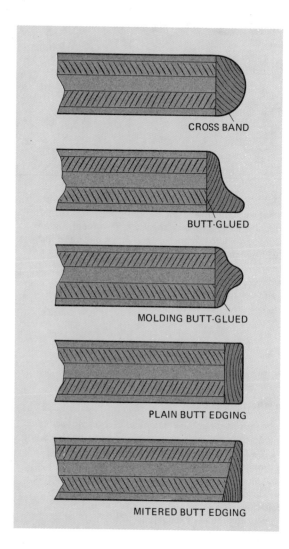

CROSS BAND

BUTT-GLUED

MOLDING BUTT-GLUED

PLAIN BUTT EDGING

MITERED BUTT EDGING

A problem from the beginning

The use of plywood in the home workshop has long presented the problem of what to do to hide the laminated edges of the material when they are exposed to view. Simplest way for the do-it-yourselfer to do it is to cover them with paper-thin wood tape which is sold in rolls in a choice of woods and merely glued on. This is okay for shelves in a bookcase and perhaps the square edges of a tabletop, but it's not too durable a treatment when the project is subject to considerable handling and wear. In being limited to plain square edges, wood tape is not the answer when you prefer that the edges of a piece of furniture be shaped. However, as shown here, there are many ways you can add eye appeal to plain plywood edges and hide the laminates in doing so. Some of the methods are comparatively simple while others are more involved

Plain butt-glue treatment

The drawings at the left show five ways you can conceal and treat straight plywood edges with a variety of moldings which are simply butt-glued. Here, of course, glue is not relied on alone; the moldings are also nailed with small finishing nails (brads in some cases) and the heads set and puttied over. A common trick for hiding nailheads is to first lift a chip of wood with a small gouge, drive the brad and then glue the chip back down. When sanded and finished the chip is hard to detect. When the project is fairly small, rubber bands cut from a large size inner tube will prove handy in holding the moldings snugly to the edges while the glue dries on the object

Edging held with splines

Where wide moldings are involved, such as those shown at the right, splines are often used to produce an exceptionally strong joint. Here saw kerfs are run in both plywood and molding on a table saw and thin wood members are ripped to fit the kerfs. If you have a means of shaping an edge, plain solid stock may be applied to the edges and the members shaped afterwards with a router or shaper. Where you wish the edge to be thicker than the plywood, such as shown in the lower detail, additional strength can be gained by a rabbet. This, plus the spline and the glue, produces a joint that can take a lot of punishment

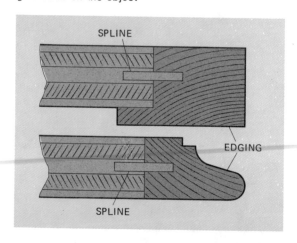

SPLINE

EDGING

SPLINE

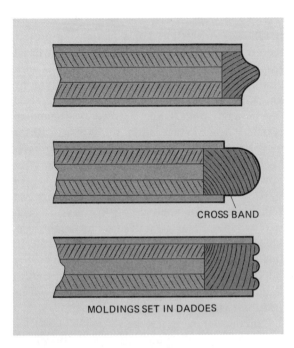

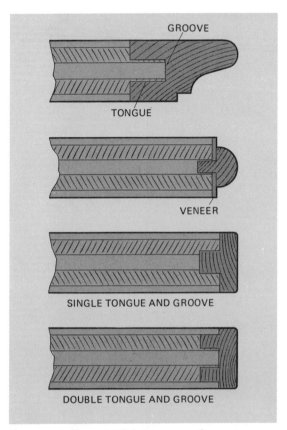

CROSS BAND

MOLDINGS SET IN DADOES

GROOVE

TONGUE

VENEER

SINGLE TONGUE AND GROOVE

DOUBLE TONGUE AND GROOVE

Moldings can be inset in dadoes

The three examples above illustrate how the top and bottom surface veneers of the plywood itself can become part of the decorative edge. In each case, a dado (groove) is made in the core laminations to a depth to suit the molding. In two examples the outer veneers form shoulders; in the other the depth of the groove, plus the molding shape, creates an edge where the veneers are held flush. Pinch clamps hold top and bottom veneers snugly to inset moldings when glued

Tongue-and-groove joints are another way

Better than being just butt-glued, decorative edges applied with tongue-and-groove joints will not pull loose readily. The top and bottom examples differ from the others above in that tongues are cut in the plywood rather than the molding. The molding conceals the entire edge either by itself or by the addition of a strip of veneer as in the second drawing

Examples of special treatments

The upper detail at the left is an example of how wide, fancy picture-frame molding can be used to treat plywood edges. As you see, a rabbet is made in the plywood edge. Later when the molding is glued in place, the top surface is sanded flush. The lower detail pictures a joint that perhaps is the strongest of all but requires special shaper cutters to form both groove and molding. In this particular treatment you can leave the molding as is or shape it

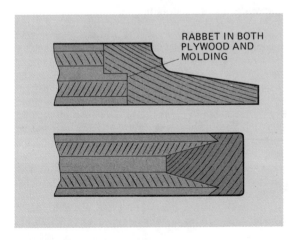

RABBET IN BOTH PLYWOOD AND MOLDING

How to remove a bearing wall

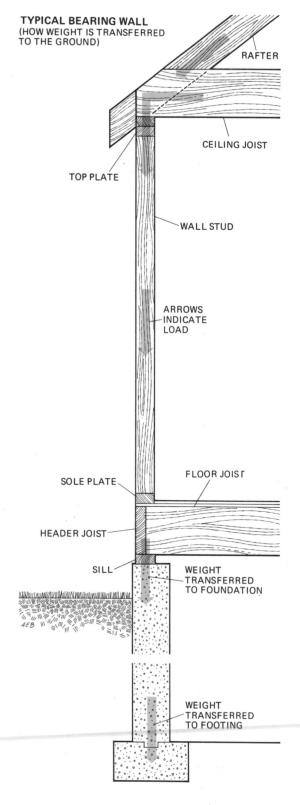

TYPICAL BEARING WALL
(HOW WEIGHT IS TRANSFERRED
TO THE GROUND)

RAFTER

CEILING JOIST

TOP PLATE

WALL STUD

ARROWS
INDICATE
LOAD

SOLE PLATE

FLOOR JOIST

HEADER JOIST

SILL

WEIGHT
TRANSFERRED
TO FOUNDATION

AEB

WEIGHT
TRANSFERRED
TO FOOTING

■ OFTEN A MAJOR home-remodeling project requires the removal of an existing wall. The usual reasons are to create a one-room effect between dining and living rooms and to enlarge a room by knocking out the wall between it and an unused bedroom or garage. Often, however, wall removal is only partial: When redecorating plans call for installation of sliding doors, for instance, or making a wide-arched opening where a single door now exists.

If the wall to be removed is simply a partition wall—that is, nonload-bearing—the task is relatively simple. But if the wall supports weight from above (see drawing, left), it is a bearing wall. In this case, it's important that a proper-size header be installed over the new opening (span) to handle the load adequately from above—and its transfer to the foundation.

Though removing a large section of a bearing wall is a job usually best left to a pro, you will be well advised to have a working knowledge of just what this task involves. Most smaller jobs can be tackled with confidence by a knowledgeable home handyman; the information on these pages will help you do that. As can be seen in the drawings and text, the first big chore is to determine whether the wall is, in fact, a bearing wall. If it is, here's how you can remove it.

Removing the wall finish

Before starting to remove the surface of any wall, determine where all electrical, heating and plumbing lines run. If any are in the wall, do not use power tools near the area. Turn off power to all outlets in the wall and use a hammer to remove plaster or drywall from these sections. Also, protect the floor with a dropcloth. Better yet, use a canvas tarp over the dropcloth. Tape the floor covering along the edges which will be walked over, or debris kicked beneath will scratch the floor. For safety, stop periodically and haul accumulated debris outside. If this is left underfoot, it can cause accidents.

The best way to remove a drywall is with a sabre saw. Simply run its blade alongside studs to make vertical cuts, and make horizontal passes to create the

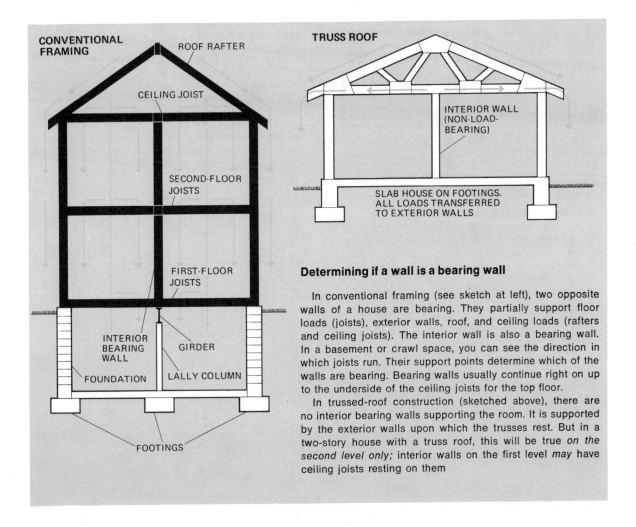

CONVENTIONAL FRAMING

ROOF RAFTER
CEILING JOIST
SECOND-FLOOR JOISTS
FIRST-FLOOR JOISTS
INTERIOR BEARING WALL
GIRDER
FOUNDATION
LALLY COLUMN
FOOTINGS

TRUSS ROOF

INTERIOR WALL (NON-LOAD-BEARING)

SLAB HOUSE ON FOOTINGS. ALL LOADS TRANSFERRED TO EXTERIOR WALLS

Determining if a wall is a bearing wall

In conventional framing (see sketch at left), two opposite walls of a house are bearing. They partially support floor loads (joists), exterior walls, roof, and ceiling loads (rafters and ceiling joists). The interior wall is also a bearing wall. In a basement or crawl space, you can see the direction in which joists run. Their support points determine which of the walls are bearing. Bearing walls usually continue right on up to the underside of the ceiling joists for the top floor.

In trussed-roof construction (sketched above), there are no interior bearing walls supporting the room. It is supported by the exterior walls upon which the trusses rest. But in a two-story house with a truss roof, this will be true *on the second level only;* interior walls on the first level *may* have ceiling joists resting on them

---

desired-size chunks. When all of the plasterboard is removed, clean the nails from all the studs you plan to save and reuse. If the studs are to be thrown out—rather foolish in these days of high lumber prices—drive home all nails before ripping out the studs.

Removing plaster and wood lath is a different—and dirtier—story. Besides protecting the floor, it's a good idea to drape dropcloths over doorways to keep white dust from spreading through the house. Open windows for ventilation and be sure to wear a face mask.

The handiest tool to have when removing a plaster wall is a bayonet-type power saw. A sabre saw does the job, too; it just takes a little longer. Use a plaster-cutting blade in either type of saw; an ordinary blade will soon become dulled and useless.

To start, make a plunge cut in one of the bays between studs and run the saw horizontally until you come to a stud. Then turn the saw in a vertical position, either up or down, and continue cutting. After you've made both horizontal cuts and one vertical cut, you can start the last vertical cut. Here you'll find that as the tool cuts into the wood lath behind the plaster, the lath chatters. Thus, it is best to have a helper hold a board against the wall on the outboard side of the saw to minimize lath chatter.

It's a good idea to give your power tool a thorough cleaning as soon as the job is completed. There will be considerable accumulation of white dust in the tool's air ports, and unless it is completely blown out, excessive heat can build up and burn out the tool.

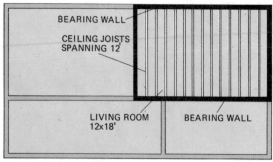

Slab-house bearing walls

In a slab house where visual inspection of the joists above is impossible, the easiest way to check which walls are bearing is by living-room dimension. If, for example, your living room measures 12x18 ft., ceiling joists will normally run the shortest dimension—12 ft. The bearing walls will be the 18-ft.-long walls. Also, it is often easy to spot the plasterboard nails in joists—by the rows of dark spots on the ceiling

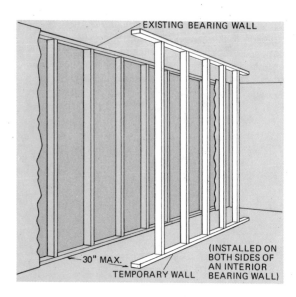

Temporarily supporting the load

Since a bearing wall denotes a wall which is supporting some structure above, it should not be removed until a temporary wall is installed (about 30 in. away from the wall). If you are removing an interior bearing wall, construct a temporary wall on both sides. A temporary supporting wall is constructed in much the same manner as a permanent wall: Studs are positioned 16 in. on centers between top and bottom plates. The main differences are that the plates are *not* nailed to the floor and ceiling, and the stud-holding nails are not toe-nailed all the way home into the plates (so they can be easily removed later).

It is important that all temporary wall studs be cut so they are a tight fit. If either ceiling or floor are uneven, use shims (undercourse shingles) between these surfaces and the plates

Installing a header

When wall studs and plates are removed, the header can be wedged up tightly under the ends of joists it will support. If required, use shims for a tight fit. If a lower header is desired, use cripple studs as shown below. The header must bear (rest) on solid wood—i.e., supporting studs, not plaster or dry wall. To make up your header, check the finished wall thickness. If the existing stud width is 3⅝ in., you'll need a ⅜-in. filler (plywood or lath) in the header

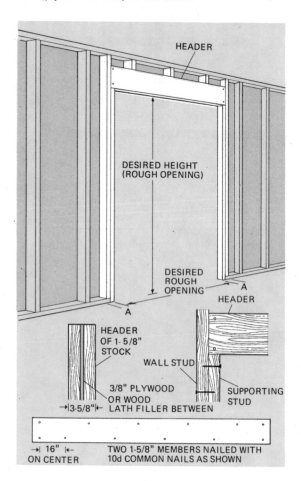

Installing new rough opening

With wall finish removed and the exact location of the desired opening determined, intermediate studs (A) may have to be installed to provide a nailer for the supporting stud or studs. With these up, the appropriate-sized header is installed, supported by a stud at each end. For openings over 6 ft., double supporting studs are required at each end of the header. For openings over 8 ft., a contractor should be employed for the job.

The chart at the bottom of the facing page is a guide for maximum loading conditions. If your room is narrower, which means less floor load, or your opening is less than that shown, your header size may be reduced. For exact sizes, consult an engineer

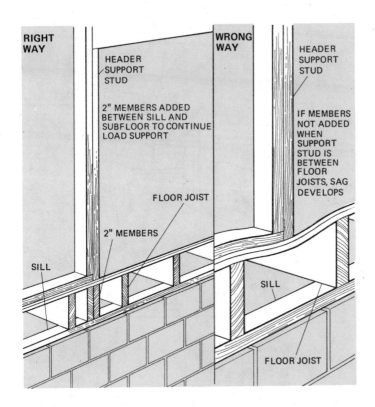

RIGHT WAY

HEADER SUPPORT STUD

2" MEMBERS ADDED BETWEEN SILL AND SUBFLOOR TO CONTINUE LOAD SUPPORT

FLOOR JOIST

2" MEMBERS

SILL

WRONG WAY

HEADER SUPPORT STUD

IF MEMBERS NOT ADDED WHEN SUPPORT STUD IS BETWEEN FLOOR JOISTS, SAG DEVELOPS

SILL

FLOOR JOIST

Supporting new load from below

Studs supporting the newly installed header must also bear on solid structure; they must not simply rest on flooring and subflooring or a serious sag will develop. In this event, the easiest solution is to cut short lengths of 2-in. members (1-⅝-in. actual dimension) equal in *length* to the *width* of the floor joists.

These "jacks" are then wedged—with grain running vertically—between the subflooring and the sill supporting the floor joists. If under an interior bearing wall, they're wedged between beam, or girder, and sub-flooring. Use at least two jack studs under each supporting stud and, when satisfied the fit is tight, secure jacks with 10d common nails.

In this way, the structure load is transferred from header to supporting studs through jack studs to the main support below. Once header and supports are installed and nailed, the temporary wall may be removed. The opening can now be finished on both sides to match the existing coverings

Finishing the job

Use plasterboard to re-cover the exposed studs in walls. If matching up to plaster thickness, add shims of wood to stud faces so that the drywall surface will be flush with the plaster wall. Spackle joints and nail-heads to finish. If your floor is of wood, it will be necessary to custom-fit a piece in the hole (where the old soleplate was). Fit the piece and install it with glue and nails through predrilled holes. Sand and finish

What size header do you need?

Header size is determined by span over the opening and weight it must support. In sketch of house at right, interior wall is a bearing wall. The chart lists header sizes needed for various widths in such a wall—with 12 ft. of floor on both sides. 2-in. stock now comes in 1½-in. actual dimension (old 1-⅝-in. size is still in stock at some yards)

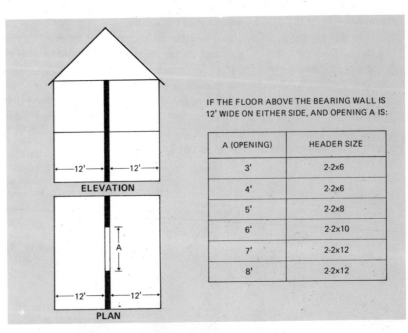

ELEVATION

PLAN

IF THE FLOOR ABOVE THE BEARING WALL IS 12' WIDE ON EITHER SIDE, AND OPENING A IS:

A (OPENING)	HEADER SIZE
3'	2-2x6
4'	2-2x6
5'	2-2x8
6'	2-2x10
7'	2-2x12
8'	2-2x12

Keep your power mower purring

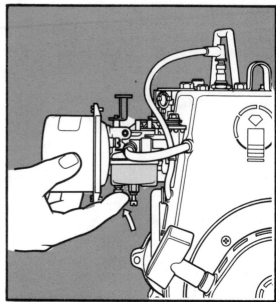

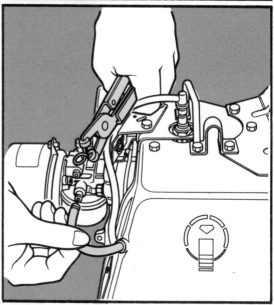

■ FAILURE TO START, hard starting and stalling are common mid-season problems that strike gasoline-powered lawnmowers and tractors. The most common causes include lack of compression, lack of or too much fuel in the cylinder, and no spark.

But a major reason for trouble can often be averted by knowing the difference between four and two-cycle engines: In four-cycle engines, ignition occurs with every fourth stroke of the piston. Four-cycle engines burn straight gasoline and possess a separate lubrication (oiling) system. It is imperative that gas and oil *not* be mixed.

In two-cycle engines, ignition occurs every second stroke of the piston. The engine runs on a mixture of oil and gasoline, and failure to mix the correct proportions of gas and oil *properly* is the single greatest cause of trouble (other than sparkplug failure). If yours is a two-cycle engine, consult the owner's manual to determine correct proportions and what kind of gas and oil is recommended. Gas and oil should be thoroughly mixed in a clean container *before* you pour it into the fuel tank.

Engine won't start

An engine won't start or will stall if fuel isn't getting to the carburetor, and from the carburetor to the cylinder. First, remove the sparkplug and inject two or three squirts of fuel into the cylinder using a clean oil can. Reinsert the plug and crank the engine. If it doesn't start, the cause of the trouble is elsewhere, but if the engine does start, runs for a few seconds and then stops, the problem will be found in the fuel system.

See if there's a drain valve in the base of the carburetor bowl. Press it (top). If no fuel leaks, there's an obstruction in the fuel line or fuel tank. If fuel leaks, there's probably an obstruction in the carburetor. If there is no drain valve, disconnect the fuel line at the bowl (bottom). If no fuel comes out, look for a blocked fuel line or obstruction in the fuel tank. If fuel leaks, a fouled carburetor is probably the cause

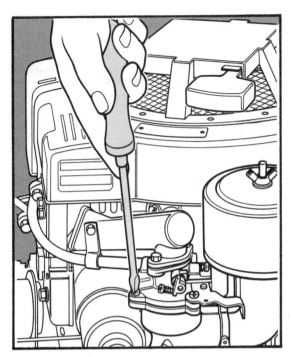 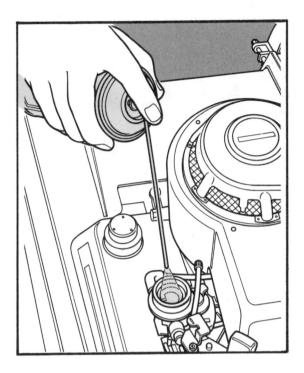

Blocked fuel line

If the fuel line is blocked, the first step is to check for contaminated fuel. Let some fuel drop into your hand; if water and dirt remain after the gas evaporates, dump all fuel and wash the fuel tank thoroughly with kerosene. It may also be necessary to clean the fuel line and carburetor.

To trouble shoot when fuel isn't getting to the carburetor:

• Replace a bent or clogged fuel line.

• Tighten all carburetor bolts, fuel-line connections and fuel-pump housing (if present) because air leaks destroy the vacuum necessary to pull fuel to the carburetor.

• Clean choke linkage and choke-plate pivots; repair damaged choke parts. Lack of choking action will make the engine hard to start; a choke stuck in the closed position will flood the engine and prevent starts.

• Clean or replace a dirty fuel filter. One kind is a wire-

mesh screen in the fuel line shutoff adapter; other engines have filter bowls.

• Replace the fuel-pump diaphragm if it has any holes.

• Clean clogged screens of fuel pipes that extend from the carburetor into the fuel tank of diaphragm-type carburetors (those without separate fuel pump).

If fuel is not getting from carburetor to engine:

• Clean the air cleaner; a dirty air cleaner causes engine flooding.

• Lightly tap the bowl of a float-type carburetor with a screwdriver to loosen a stuck needle valve .

• Adjust the carburetor. Turn the idle-mixture needle in until finger-tight, then back out one turn. Adjust the idle speed by backing out the adjusting screw, then turning it in until it just touches the throttle lever—then give it one more full turn.

• Finally, disassemble the carburetor and give it a thorough cleaning.

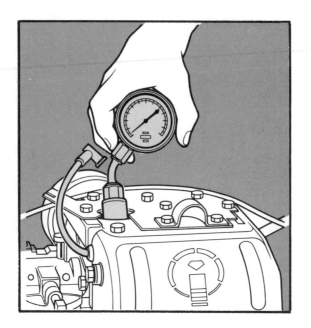

Inadequate compression

Stated simply, compression is the ability of the piston to compress the fuel/air mixture. Inadequate compression leads to hard starting and loss of power. Poor compression results when a cylinder is scored, piston rings stick or wear, valves stick or wear, or the crankshaft oil seal is damaged. The pressure loss reduces compression, which makes ignition more difficult.

One obvious sign that there is compression loss is a sloppy manual starting cord. If the cord offers little resistance and doesn't snap back, then sufficient compression is questionable.

An accurate check can be made with a compression gauge. Remove the sparkplug, insert the gauge fitting firmly, and crank the engine until the gauge reaches its maximum reading. The *minimum* compression of two-cycle engines is 60 psi; of four-cycles of 4½ hp or less, 65 psi; and of four-cycles above 4½ hp, 70 psi.

Compression loss may be caused by a loose sparkplug. Seat the plug by hand and give it one-half turn with a socket wrench .

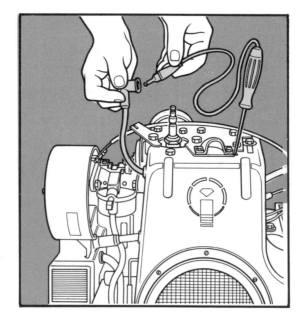

Garden tractors

Garden tractors with high-horsepower engines usually have transformer-coil ignition systems that are like those in cars, but must powermowers use a magneto system. Magnetos make their own electricity by a magnet-equipped flywheel that revolves around stationary field coils.

You can test a magneto system by gapping either a 14-mm or an 18-mm sparkplug to 5/32-3/16-in. Attach it to the sparkplug lead and ground it against the cylinder head as you crank the engine. A blue spark should jump the electrode gap.

The same test can be made of a transformer-coil ignition system, but use the engine's sparkplug at its normal gap.

Use a spark-intensity tester for checking breakerless systems (left). Disconnect the lead from the sparkplug and attach the tester to the lead's metal terminal. Touch the test instrument's probe to a ground as you crank the engine. The test light will flash if the system is operating properly.

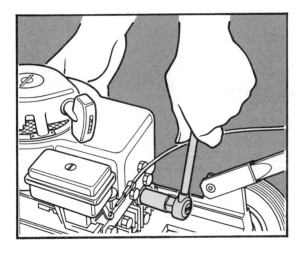

About sparkplugs

The sparkplug is one of the biggest single causes of engine problems. First, check the owner's manual to make sure you're using the right one. Then make certain the plug lead is connected tightly to the plug terminal, and to the magneto or coil output. If the lead's insulation is cracked, replace the lead. Buy a new sparkplug if the insulator is damaged or if electrodes are worn, burned or heavily coated with carbon or oil. Carbon on a plug usually means an engine is operating on an overly rich fuel mixture or that the ignition output is below par; oil on electrodes usually means that piston rings or valve stems (four-cycle engine) are worn; burned electrodes indicate that the engine is probably overheating.

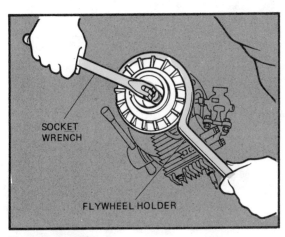

SOCKET WRENCH

FLYWHEEL HOLDER

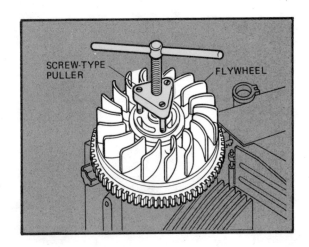

SCREW-TYPE PULLER

FLYWHEEL

Magneto repair

To repair a magneto ignition you have to remove the flywheel. On most two-cycle engines, first remove the flywheel nut. Some of these nuts have a right-hand thread; others, left-hand. If the flywheel moves as you turn the nut, hold it fast with a flywheel holder. With the nut off, it can usually be removed. On most four-cycle engines, hold the flywheel with a flywheel holder as the flywheel nut is removed. Install a knockout puller, hold the flywheel firmly, and rap the puller with a hammer to jar the flywheel loose.

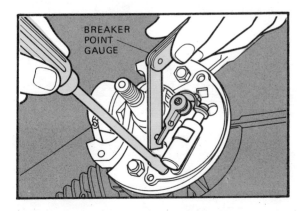

BREAKER POINT GAUGE

More about magnetos

Magneto repairs also involve checking all leads for tightness and cleanliness, and testing high-tension wires to assure that no shorts exist. Replace breaker points if they are burned or pitted. Replace the condenser each time you change breaker points. Gap points to .020 inch (double-check the gap in the owner's manual). Test the ignition output again. Now if the system fails to respond, a major overhaul is called for, including the replacement of coils and magnets, and the timing system.

Tabletop and benchtops are made of clear-pine 2x8s doweled and edge-glued. Pegged stretchers add a great deal of rigidity to the table and benches

Build a beautiful trestle table

BY EVERETT JOHNSON

Simple in appearance but rugged and durable, here is an
easy-to-build piece that is sure to become a family heirloom

SERVING SIX PEOPLE comfortably, as well as offering the rugged good looks of Early American pine furniture, this hand-pegged, trestle dining table is a period piece you'll use and admire for years to come. Its beauty lies in its simplicity, both in design and construction. Best of all, it's made of common clear pine, which means you can get the wood to make it at any lumberyard.

Except for size, the two trestle benches are duplicates of the table, the main difference being the number of pieces required to build up the 30-in. wide top. The 1½-in.-thick stock, which is used for the table and benchtops, is doweled and glued together edgewise, then clamped. When the glue is dry, top surfaces of the built-up members are planed smooth, sanded with a medium-abrasive belt on a belt sander, or by hand, then the top edges are rounded.

The leg patterns for benches and table are similar, and all six legs are sabre-sawed from 1⅛-in.-thick pine. Some lumberyards have 1⅛-in. pine 14 in. wide. Where you can't obtain this width, the stock for the table legs will have to be doweled and glued up like the tabletop. The open mortises in the legs are made 1⅛ in. wide to accept the shouldered ends of the stretchers. The mortises are easily cut with a sabre saw by first boring a ½-in. hole for the saw blade. Cleat and foot members are cut to the sizes given and are attached to the scroll-cut legs with ½-in. dowels.

turn the page

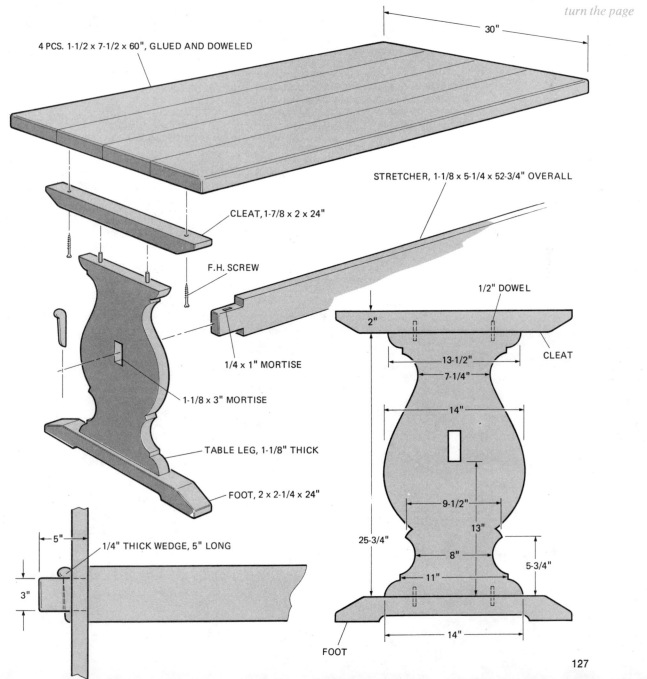

4 PCS. 1-1/2 x 7-1/2 x 60", GLUED AND DOWELED

30"

STRETCHER, 1-1/8 x 5-1/4 x 52-3/4" OVERALL

CLEAT, 1-7/8 x 2 x 24"

F.H. SCREW

1/4 x 1" MORTISE

1-1/8 x 3" MORTISE

TABLE LEG, 1-1/8" THICK

FOOT, 2 x 2-1/4 x 24"

1/4" THICK WEDGE, 5" LONG

5"

3"

1/2" DOWEL

2"

13-1/2"

7-1/4"

14"

CLEAT

9-1/2"

13"

25-3/4"

8"

5-3/4"

11"

14"

FOOT

127

Sabre saw makes quick work of sawing out scrolled
table and bench legs. Feed the saw slowly, follow the
lines closely, then sand the edges with abrasive blocks

Counterbored holes in the cleats permit husky
screws to be used to anchor the legs to the table
and benchtops.

A ¼ x 1-in. open mortise is made vertically in
the stretcher tenons for ¼-in. tapered wedges.
The mortises are located at a point which will
draw the tenon shoulders tightly against the leg
when the wedges are tapped in place.

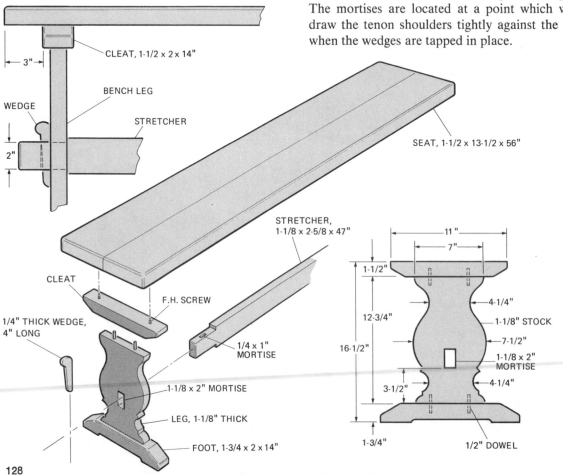

CLEAT, 1-1/2 x 2 x 14"

3"

WEDGE

BENCH LEG

STRETCHER

2"

SEAT, 1-1/2 x 13-1/2 x 56"

STRETCHER,
1-1/8 x 2-5/8 x 47"

CLEAT

F.H. SCREW

1/4" THICK WEDGE,
4" LONG

1/4 x 1"
MORTISE

1-1/8 x 2" MORTISE

LEG, 1-1/8" THICK

FOOT, 1-3/4 x 2 x 14"

11"

7"

1-1/2"

4-1/4"

12-3/4"

1-1/8" STOCK

7-1/2"

16-1/2"

1-1/8 x 2"
MORTISE

4-1/4"

3-1/2"

1-3/4"

1/2" DOWEL

Telephone caddy

BY ELMER E. SCOTT

■ HOW MANY TIMES have you wanted to jot down a telephone message only to find no pencil or paper handy? It won't happen with this telephone caddy. Serving as a base for a cradle phone, it is fitted with a drawer for pad and phone list, and a pencil groove.

Both the bottom of the box and the back of the box are housed in rabbets cut in the side members. Those housing the back are blind rabbets which stop ¼-in. from the top. The ³⁄₁₆ x ¼-in. grooves for the drawer guides are run, of course, before final assembly. The top of the box, grooved to fit over the side members, butts the top of the back.

While dimensions are given for the drawer, the job is to fit it so it slides easily into the box. The lipped drawer front laps all four edges of the box flush.

After the box is assembled, finish it to suit your personal taste.

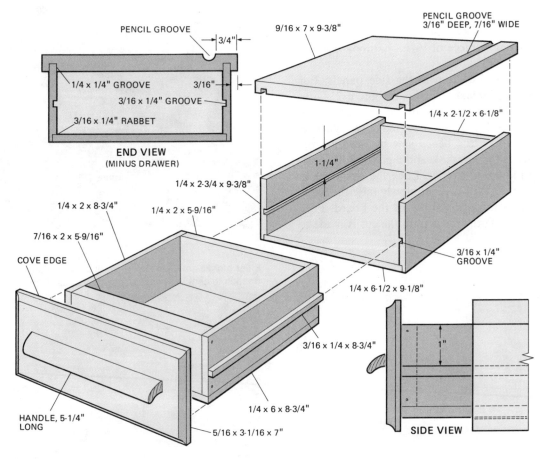

PENCIL GROOVE

3/4"

PENCIL GROOVE
3/16" DEEP, 7/16" WIDE

9/16 x 7 x 9-3/8"

1/4 x 1/4" GROOVE   3/16"

3/16 x 1/4" GROOVE

3/16 x 1/4" RABBET

1/4 x 2-1/2 x 6-1/8"

END VIEW
(MINUS DRAWER)

1-1/4"

1/4 x 2-3/4 x 9-3/8"

1/4 x 2 x 8-3/4"

1/4 x 2 x 5-9/16"

7/16 x 2 x 5-9/16"

COVE EDGE

3/16 x 1/4"
GROOVE

1/4 x 6-1/2 x 9-1/8"

3/16 x 1/4 x 8-3/4"

1"

HANDLE, 5-1/4"
LONG

1/4 x 6 x 8-3/4"

5/16 x 3-1/16 x 7"

SIDE VIEW

Pier curio shelf

BY ROSARIO CAPOTOSTO

Not only is this a display
cabinet for your curios, but it is also a
handsome decoration for any wall
in your home. It can be built
of common pine for a very reasonable price

■ THIS CHARMING curio shelf will do won-
ders in showing off your most prized pieces of
bric-a-brac, as well as making a handsome wall
decoration itself. It is not difficult to make and
can be fashioned from wood that is easy to obtain
at a reasonable price. It cost me about $5 for
14 ft. of ½ x 8-in. common pine, a short length of
cove molding, a piece of ⅛-in. hardboard and a
wooden drawer knob.

Construction starts with the side panels. For
an easy way to make the cutouts, bore a 2¼-in.-
diameter hole as indicated in the drawing. Then,
using a smooth-cutting blade, make two parallel
internal cuts on the bench saw by lowering the
blade below the saw table and then carefully positioning the board over it. Lock the rip fence in
place, turn on the saw, then slowly raise the blade
until it cuts through the top of the board. Feed
the work along the fence until the cut is made to

Filler blocks are glued to the ends of each of the
dadoes to conceal (make blind) the exposed grooves

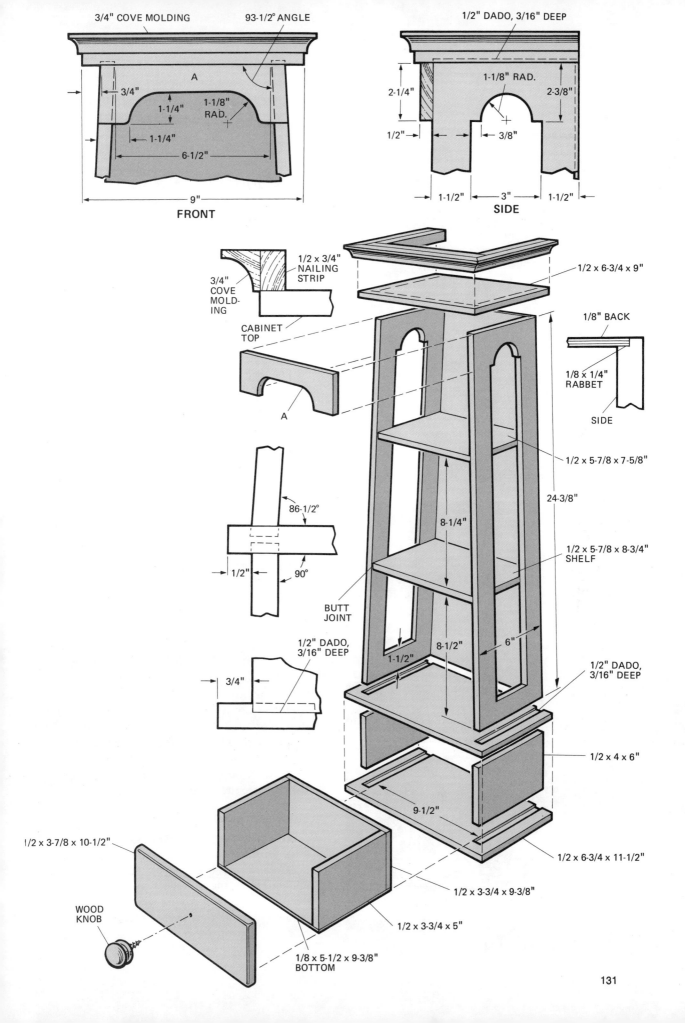

FRONT

3/4" COVE MOLDING

93-1/2° ANGLE

A

3/4"

1-1/4"

1-1/8" RAD.

1-1/4"

6-1/2"

9"

SIDE

1/2" DADO, 3/16" DEEP

2-1/4"

1-1/8" RAD.

2-3/8"

1/2"

3/8"

1-1/2"

3"

1-1/2"

1/2 x 3/4" NAILING STRIP

3/4" COVE MOLD-ING

CABINET TOP

A

86-1/2°

1/2"

90°

BUTT JOINT

1/2" DADO, 3/16" DEEP

3/4"

1/2 x 6-3/4 x 9"

1/8" BACK

1/8 x 1/4" RABBET

SIDE

1/2 x 5-7/8 x 7-5/8"

24-3/8"

8-1/4"

1/2 x 5-7/8 x 8-3/4" SHELF

8-1/2"

6"

1-1/2"

1/2" DADO, 3/16" DEEP

1/2 x 4 x 6"

9-1/2"

1/2 x 6-3/4 x 11-1/2"

1/2 x 3-7/8 x 10-1/2"

1/2 x 3-3/4 x 9-3/8"

1/2 x 3-3/4 x 5"

WOOD KNOB

1/8 x 5-1/2 x 9-3/8" BOTTOM

curio shelf, continued

the length required. Cut off the power and wait until the blade comes to a full stop before taking the board away. Make the final corner cuts with a sabre saw to drop out the waste.

dado for side panels

Angled dado cuts are required to seat the side panels into the upper and lower cross members. Tilt the dado blade to a 86½° angle for these cuts. Blind dadoes are not necessary in any of the joints. Run the cuts through, then simply cut filler blocks and glue them into the exposed ends to fill the voids. This method will prove simpler and quicker than making blind dadoes. A ⅛ x ¼-in. rabbet is required at the rear of the side panels and the top and lowermost members to form a recess for the hardboard back panel. Sand all parts before you begin to assemble the shelf.

The two open shelves need not be set into dadoes as the other parts. Simple butt joints will do the job here. Carefully cut them to the exact length with the appropriate bevel so they will fit snuggly against the sides. They can be secured by using finishing nails and glue. The top trim of the shelf looks like fancy router work, but is simply molding. Cove molding, ¾-in., is used for this trim work. Since its profile does not permit direct nailing to the top, small nailing strips are added to the back of the molding. Cut 45° miters to join the molding.

The finish is optional depending on your personal preferences. You can use stain, shellac, clear varnish or paint, or you may want to try a woodgraining finish. For the last, use a latex-based woodgraining or antiquing kit of the desired tone for quick results. Coat the surfaces with the latex-base coat and allow to dry (this usually takes about one hour). Then apply the glaze coat, working one main section at a time. Run a dry brush over the still wet glaze to produce the "grain." If the result is not quite what you want, simply wipe off the glaze and try again (you can't fail). If you want to highlight the corners, as was done here, run a dry rag pad over them before the glaze dries.

install back panel last

The hardboard back panel should be installed after finishing for an easier, neater job. Instead of graining the back panel, you may consider applying only the base coat to it. This will produce a neutral background which will allow your curios to stand out more clearly. Bore a hole near the top of the back panel for hanging on a screw.

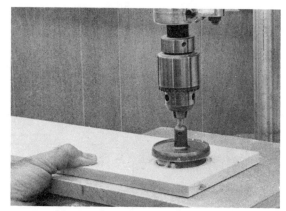

A hole saw is used in your drill press to make a circular cut at the top of the side panels

Waste is removed by raising the rotating blade and pushing the stock forward or backward

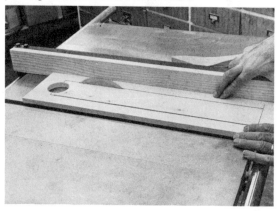

A sabre saw is used to complete the parallel cuts to the very corners to drop out the remaining waste

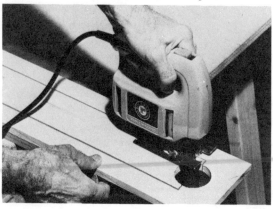

BY WALTER E. BURTON

Cloth tape inlays

Shallow channels are first routed to equal thickness of the tape, then corners are squared with chisel

Ends of tape are mitered by holding sharp wood chisel against 45° template and cutting over hardboard

White glue is spread evenly in channels, then tape is pressed in place. Wipe excess glue with damp cloth

■ AT FIRST GLANCE, the colorful design on the lid of this trinket box looks like expensive enameled inlay work. Actually it's nothing more than patterned fabric tape cemented in shallow channels and coated with a clear plastic finish, but the simulation is nearly perfect.

Any fancy cloth tape, ¼ to 1-in. wide, can be used this way; a metallic braid will produce a handsome inlay of delicately wrought gold bands.

The picture sequence shows how you first create $\frac{1}{32}$-in.-deep channels for the tape with a router and chisel. Then you miter the tape like the corners of a picture frame with a 45° template and a wood chisel, after which you apply white glue sparingly to the channels and press the tape in place flush with the surface.

Finally, you finish both box lid and cloth tape with two coats of a transparent urethane to enhance the wood grain and bring out the beauty of the tape pattern.

When glue is dry, tape is given two coats of clear urethane finish, finally the rest of the wood surface

Build a buffet-bed table

BY WAYNE C. LECKEY

Covered with wood-grain plastic laminate, this multipurpose
table earns its keep in many ways. With leaves extended it's a buffet counter.
Straddling a twin bed it makes a handy bed table

■ STANDING BY TO SERVE a dual role, this double-duty buffet-bed table will prove to be one of the handiest pieces of furniture in your home. As a buffet table with its drop leaves extended, it becomes a 7-ft. long counter.

When used during sickness or just for breakfast in bed, the table can straddle a twin-size bed and let you eat, read, or write in comfort. Rolled to the foot of the bed, the table affords a perfect viewing place for a portable TV set.

From its handsome wood-grain finish you'd never know it was made from common fir plywood and pine lumber. All exposed surfaces are faced with Formica's English Oak laminate to provide a durable finish. The table's height must

be determined by the particular bed, since some beds are higher than others. Likewise, the table should be wide enough to clear the sides of the bed by a couple of inches.

Basically, the table consists of four separate parts: two built-up legs, a top assembly and a countertop. The latter (including its drop leaves) goes on last after you've covered it with laminate and hinged the leaves. As you will note in studying the drawing, the top assembly has two same-size (top and bottom) frames of doweled 1x2s (¾ x 1½ in.) which are glued and nailed flush to 3¼-in. side rails (B, C and D) and a center divider (A).

The top frame differs in that it has cross mem-

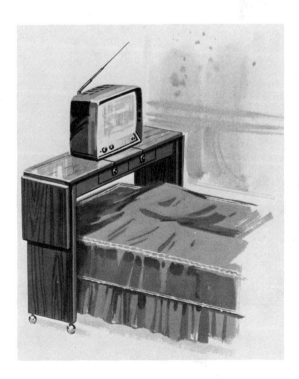

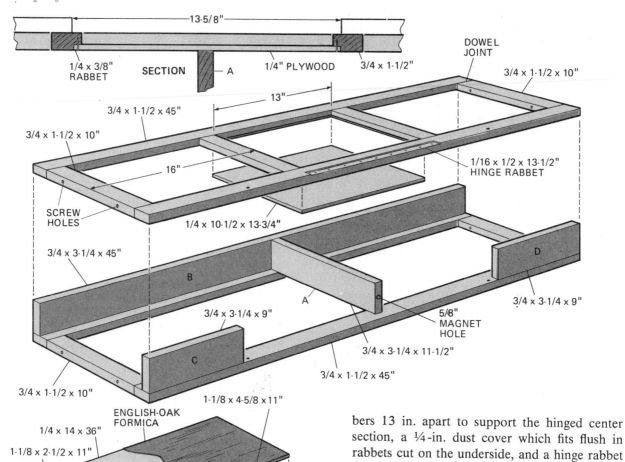

13-5/8"

1/4 x 3/8"
RABBET

SECTION — A

1/4" PLYWOOD

3/4 1-1/2"

DOWEL
JOINT

3/4 x 1-1/2 x 10"

3/4 x 1-1/2 x 45"

13"

3/4 x 1-1/2 x 10"

16"

1/16 x 1/2 x 13-1/2"
HINGE RABBET

SCREW
HOLES

1/4 x 10-1/2 x 13-3/4"

3/4 x 3-1/4 x 45"

B

D

A

3/4 x 3-1/4 x 9"

3/4 x 3-1/4 x 9"

5/8"
MAGNET
HOLE

C

3/4 x 3-1/4 x 11-1/2"

3/4 x 1-1/2 x 10"

3/4 x 1-1/2 x 45"

1-1/8 x 4-5/8 x 11"

ENGLISH-OAK
FORMICA

1/4 x 14 x 36"

1-1/8 x 2-1/2 x 11"

1-1/8 x 1-1/2 x 36"

1-1/8 x 2 x 11"

CASTER
SOCKET

LEG SANDWICH DETAIL

bers 13 in. apart to support the hinged center section, a ¼-in. dust cover which fits flush in rabbets cut on the underside, and a hinge rabbet for the book rack (see section view). Each end member is drilled before assembly for two ¼ x 3-in. screws which are used to attach the legs, and a ⅝-in.-diameter hole is made in the end of center divider (A) for a button magnet. Screw holes are also made in the two frames for the drawer pivots although these holes can be made after assembly.

An 8½-in. wrought-iron hinge screwed to the underside of the bookrack is used as a prop

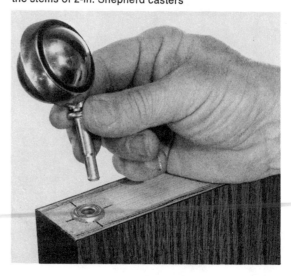

Sockets driven in the ends of the table legs accept the stems of 2-in. Shepherd casters

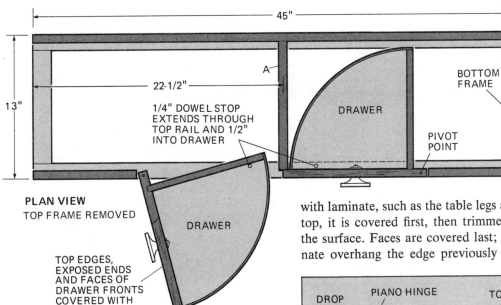

PLAN VIEW
TOP FRAME REMOVED

45"

13"

22-1/2"

1/4" DOWEL STOP
EXTENDS THROUGH
TOP RAIL AND 1/2"
INTO DRAWER

A

DRAWER

BOTTOM
FRAME

PIVOT
POINT

DRAWER

TOP EDGES,
EXPOSED ENDS
AND FACES OF
DRAWER FRONTS
COVERED WITH
FORMICA

The two built-up legs are identical, each consisting of an inner frame of 1⅛-in. pine and faced on each side with ¼-in. plywood. Note that the inner top member of each leg is wider than the others, and that holes for the caster sockets are made in the lower ends of the side members.

To apply the Formica, cut the 1/16-in.-thick laminate a bit larger than the wood surface to be covered and "glue" it in place with contact cement. The latter is applied with a brush to both wood and laminate, allowed to dry until tacky to the touch, then the surfaces are joined. Bond is instant; once the two coated surfaces touch, they can't be shifted. Therefore, it's necessary that the laminate be positioned carefully the first time.

When in place, the laminate is tapped all over with a hammer and wood block to assure good contact and bond. When an edge is to be covered

with laminate, such as the table legs and countertop, it is covered first, then trimmed flush with the surface. Faces are covered last; let the laminate overhang the edge previously covered ap-

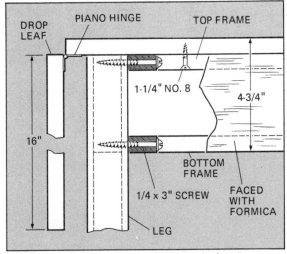

DROP
LEAF

PIANO HINGE

TOP FRAME

1-1/4" NO. 8

4-3/4"

16"

BOTTOM
FRAME

1/4 x 3" SCREW

FACED
WITH
FORMICA

LEG

The cutaway drawing above shows how long wood screws through holes in the end rails are used to attach the top section rigidly to the hollow table legs. The screws enter wide blocking inside the legs at the top. The legs are attached before the countertop and drop leaves have been added to the table

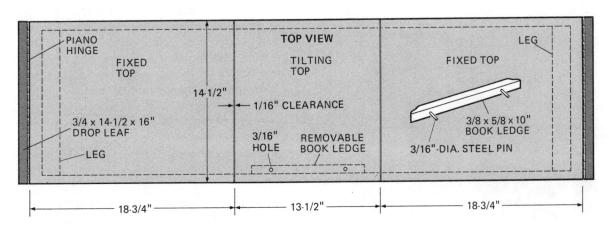

PIANO
HINGE

TOP VIEW

LEG

FIXED
TOP

TILTING
TOP

FIXED TOP

14-1/2"

1/16" CLEARANCE

3/4 x 14-1/2 x 16"
DROP LEAF

3/16"
HOLE

REMOVABLE
BOOK LEDGE

3/8 x 5/8 x 10"
BOOK LEDGE

LEG

3/16"-DIA. STEEL PIN

18-3/4"

13-1/2"

18-3/4"

Quarter-circle drawers swing open on screw pivots driven through the rails from above and below. The ledge strip at the bottom of the slanting book-rack is removable when the table is used for buffet serving. Short sections of 20d nail in the ledge strip fit mating holes in the book rack

DRAWER DETAIL
MAKE RIGHT AND LEFT HAND

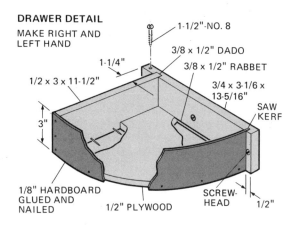

1-1/2"-NO. 8
3/8 x 1/2" DADO
3/8 x 1/2" RABBET
1-1/4"
1/2 x 3 x 11-1/2"
3/4 x 3-1/6 x 13-5/16"
SAW KERF
3"
1/8" HARDBOARD GLUED AND NAILED
1/2" PLYWOOD
SCREW-HEAD
1/2"

The drop leaves are supported by standard leaf supports made by Stanley, New Britain, Conn.

proximately ⅛ in., then trim as before. Trimming is done quickly and professionally with a portable router and special cutter, but it can be done by hand with a flat mill file. Be careful not to scratch the finished surface of the laminate.

The front and back surfaces of the top assembly are faced with 4¾-in.-wide pieces of laminate. Like the back, the front is covered with a single piece, then cut out over the drawer opening and filed even with the frame edges and ends of pieces C and D.

The right and left-hand drawer fronts are fitted to their openings so there is a ¹⁄₁₆-in. clearance top and bottom after they are faced with laminate. A thin washer placed over the pivot screw maintains this clearance at the bottom. The two drawers meet in the center of divider (A). They are held shut by flathead screws which contact the magnet. The latter, which is available from J. C. Armor Co., Inc., Box 290, Deer Park, N. Y. 11729, is set flush and glued in its hole.

Lengths of brass-plated piano hinge (cut 14½ in. long) are used to hinge the drop leaves to the 18¾-in. counter sections. Here all four edges of the five-piece counter are banded with laminate before the top surfaces are covered. Finally, 1¼-in. No. 8 wood screws are driven from below through the top frame to attach the counter.

An heirloom footstool

Here's a craft project you can make in your shop which is a real
Early American beauty. It will be at home among your treasured period pieces

BY ELMER E. SCOTT

■ ARE YOU LOOKING for a gift for a friend or relative? Or perhaps you are an Early American furniture buff. No matter which, this charming footstool will be a prized possession, and will take a special place in anybody's living room. You make it yourself and can bring out its full beauty by giving its walnut frame a fine hand-rubbed finish and its padded upholstered top your most careful attention.

The three-piece side frames are identical, as are the end rails and turned spindles. There are two ways you can tackle the 1-in.-thick side frames: 1. Blank stock for the legs can be glued and doweled to blank rails and the assembly bandsawed as a single piece. 2. The three pieces can be laid out and cut separately and then glued and doweled together. No matter which of the two

way you use it, you'll have to begin by first making a full-size cardboard leg pattern following the grid drawing. If you cut the parts individually, you'll do well to bore the $\frac{3}{8}$-in. dowel holes in the ends of the curved rails before bandsawing so you'll have maximum support for your doweling jig.

Both the side and end rails require a $\frac{3}{16}$ x $\frac{3}{4}$-in. rabbet in the top edges for tacking the upholstery. The end-rail rabbets can be cut easily on your table saw; those in the curved side rails will require a router or shaper. If a router is used, it's used on the flat side of the rails and with a straight router bit. A circular guide attached to the router's base is used to follow the curved edge and set the depth of cut.

The spindles are tenoned turnings glued in

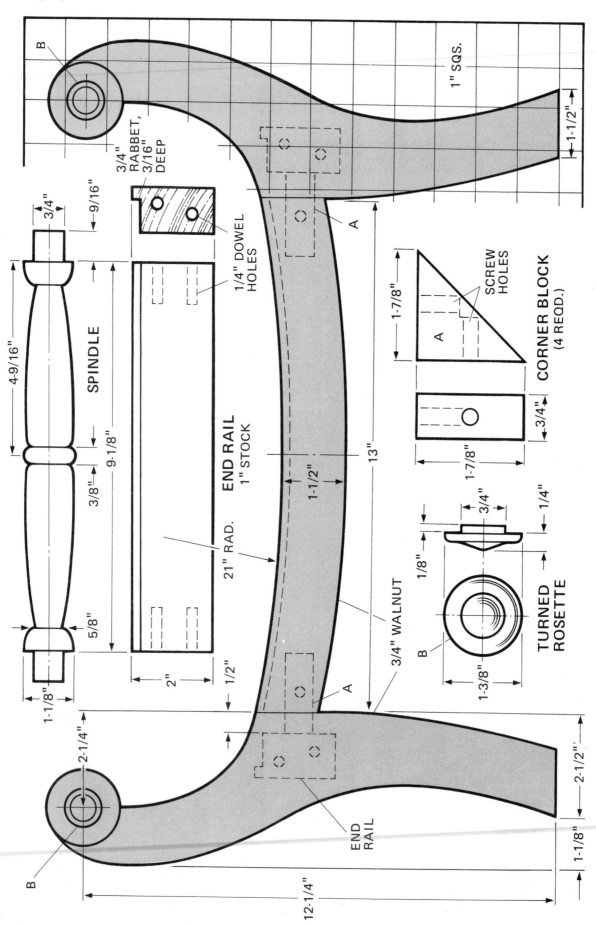

1" SQS.

1-1/2"

B

3/4" RABBET, 3/16" DEEP

1/4" DOWEL HOLES

A

A

3/4"
9/16"

4-9/16"

SPINDLE

9-1/8"

3/8"

5/8"

2"

1/2"

END RAIL
1" STOCK

21" RAD.

1-1/2"

13"

3/4" WALNUT

1-1/8"

2-1/4"

B

12-1/4"

END RAIL

A

2-1/2"

1-1/8"

1-7/8"

SCREW HOLES

A

CORNER BLOCK
(4 REQD.)

3/4"

1-7/8"

3/4"

1/8"

1/4"

B

1-3/8"

TURNED
ROSETTE

First, webbing is stretched across the stool frame. Then foam padding is placed on top and this is finally covered by your choice of upholstery

Tenons are formed at each end of the turned spindles. These will fit in the ¾-in holes which you have bored in the side frames

¾-in. holes that are bored completely through the side frames. Turned rosettes are used to cap the spindle holes on the face side. Both spindles and end rails must be glued and clamped in place at the same time, of course and triangular glue blocks are added at the four corners.

All exposed wood surfaces of your footstool should be completely finished before the stool is upholstered.

The first step in padding the top is to stretch black cambric from rail to rail and tack it in the rabbets. Then strips of furniture webbing are laced crisscross over the cambric and the turned-under edges tacked to the rabbets. A 2-in. thickness of foam rubber or other padding comes next, then the top covering. The edges of the latter are folded under and tacked neatly to the rabbets. Finally, ½-in.-wide braid and roundhead upholstery nails, 74 in all, spaced about ¾-in. apart, are used to add a finished touch to the padded top.

You can stow away this patio table

For about $75 you can build this handsome
picnic table. It is designed to fold up to a compact
2x5 feet so it can be stored easily

BY WAYNE C. LECKEY

■ IT'S GREAT TO HAVE a big table out on
your deck or patio for those pleasant summer-
evening meals. But finding a place to store it is
something else. Often it simply stays outdoors
all year.

We tossed the storage problem at designer
Tom Fung, well known for his unique designs,
who came up with the ingenious folding table you
see here. Eighteen pivot points make it possible
to fold the table into an incredibly small space of
2x5 feet, which means you can park it in a garage
or basement with room to spare.

142

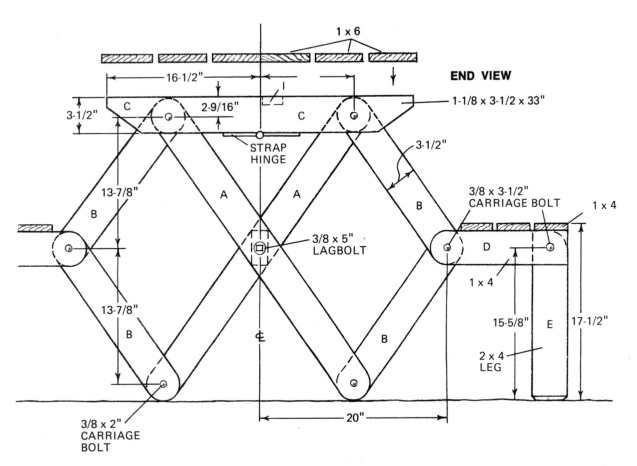

END VIEW

1 x 6

16-1/2"

3-1/2"

2-9/16"

STRAP HINGE

1-1/8 x 3-1/2 x 33"

3-1/2"

13-7/8"

A   A

B   B

3/8 x 3-1/2"
CARRIAGE BOLT

1 x 4

3/8 x 5"
LAGBOLT

D

1 x 4

C̶

13-7/8"

B   B

15-5/8"

E

17-1/2"

2 x 4
LEG

3/8 x 2"
CARRIAGE
BOLT

20"

HINGE JOINT

1-1/2" NO. 10
FH SCREWS

COUNTERBORED
HOLES FOR 1/4 x 3"
CARRIAGE BOLTS

C

CARRIAGE
BOLTS

5" STRAP HINGE

C   C

NEW HOLES
DRILLED IN
HINGE

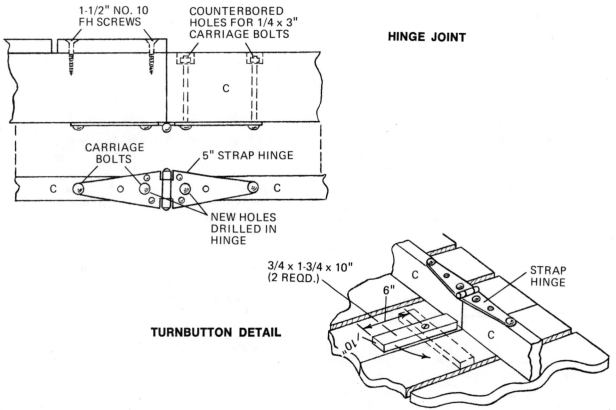

3/4 x 1-3/4 x 10"
(2 REQD.)

6"

C

STRAP
HINGE

C

10"

TURNBUTTON DETAIL

143

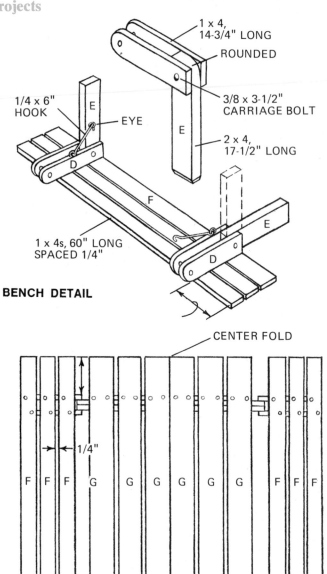

1 x 4,
14-3/4" LONG

ROUNDED

1/4 x 6"
HOOK

E

EYE

3/8 x 3-1/2"
CARRIAGE BOLT

E

2 x 4,
17-1/2" LONG

D

F

E

1 x 4s, 60" LONG
SPACED 1/4"

D

BENCH DETAIL

CENTER FOLD

1/4"

F F F G G G G G F F F

TABLETOP

MATERIALS NEEDED (Redwood)

Key	Size	Amt.
A	¾ x 3½ x 38"	4
B	¾ x 3½ x 20¾"	8
C	1⅛ x 3½ x 16½"	4
D	¾ x 3½ x 14¾"	8
E	1½ x 3½ x 17½"	4
F	¾ x 3½ x 60"	6
G	¾ x 5½ x 60"	6
H	1½ x 3½ x 34¾"	1
I	¾ x 1¾ x 10"	2

Hardware

¼ x 3" carriage bolts	8
¼ x 3½" carriage bolts	4
¼ x 2" carriage bolts	4
1¼" No. 10 FH wood screws	2
1½" No. 10 FH wood screws	48
¼ x 6" hooks and eyes	4
5" strap hinges	2
Cadmium-plated washers	34

We built the prototype, from long-lasting redwood, for a material cost of about $75. If you use No. 2 pine and paint it, it can be made for less. While it may look difficult, it's actually an easy table to build, mainly because all the parts are of lumberyard size which you just cut to length.

The table is identical each side of a centerline. Each bench is alike, as is each scissor-folding leg. Spotting the seven pivot holes for each leg is done best by marking their locations on a sheet of plywood or wrapping paper and drilling the holes in the leg members to correspond. Round the ends of the members to a 1¾-in. radius and drill holes at the compass points. A good stunt to follow when rounding the ends and drilling the holes is to do two or more ends at one time by clamping the members together. This assures perfect alignment of the holes and makes for a neater job.

Cut parts C, to which the six tabletop members are attached, from 1⅛-in.-thick stock and join them endwise with 5-in. strap hinges. Drill an additional hole in each hinge leaf for a second carriage bolt. Use wood turnbuttons to lock the tabletop in the open position; place them on the underside near the hinges, on opposite sides of the centerline. You can keep the bench legs from being kicked outward accidentally by use of king-size hooks and eyes, and drawing up the carriage bolts holding the legs snugly so the legs do not swing freely. Place three large washers between leg members at each point where the benches attach, elsewhere, just one washer. Place washers under all nuts, of course.

Cookbook caddy

BY ROSARIO CAPOTOSTO

■ THIS HANDSOME SHELF will add a touch of interest to your kitchen and keep your wife's cookbooks handy at the same time. Its drawer can store recipes galore.

There are no fancy joints to bother with; nothing but butt joints, glued and nailed, are used. The back and the drawer interior are cut from plywood, but ½-in. solid pine is used for the rest. Set your rip fence to make 12-in. cuts and run all at one time to insure a perfect fit for all inside pieces

and to save yourself time. Saw the curves, then use your router with a ¼-round bit to round the edges where indicated. Sand all surfaces as smooth as you will want them before you begin the assembly.

Assemble the parts with glue and 1½-in. finishing nails in this order: First attach the base apron to the drawer shelf. Then attach the back to both shelves and add the sides. Set the nailheads and fill the holes. Make the plywood drawer as a box with four sides and a bottom, then add the pine false front and the knob. For an interesting finish, that is not too difficult, try a wood graining or antiquing kit.

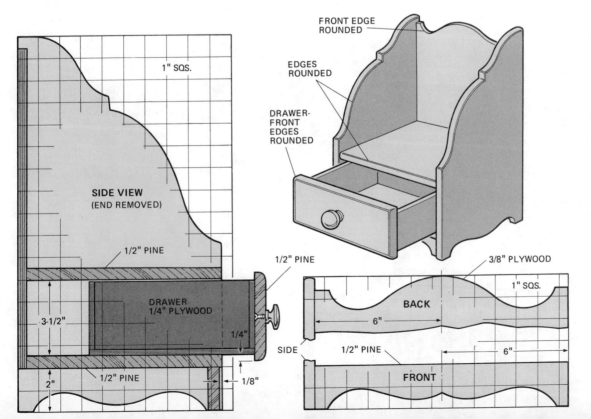

1" SQS.

SIDE VIEW
(END REMOVED)

1/2" PINE

DRAWER
1/4" PLYWOOD

3-1/2"

1/2" PINE

2"

1/4"

1/8"

FRONT EDGE
ROUNDED

EDGES
ROUNDED

DRAWER-
FRONT
EDGES
ROUNDED

1/2" PINE

3/8" PLYWOOD

1" SQS.

BACK

6"

6"

SIDE

1/2" PINE

FRONT

145

Tilt the drill-press table so a pencil line on the leg and drill bit are vertical, then clamp

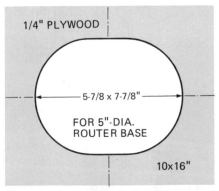

1/4" PLYWOOD

5-7/8 x 7-7/8"

FOR 5"-DIA. ROUTER BASE

10x16"

A template forms mortises for both leaves of hinges in one quick router operation to save time

Build a butler's table

By ROSARIO CAPOTOSTO

Make this butler's table with a lift-off top, and you'll always be ready to serve coffee or tea to guests. With the top on the base, it's a handsome coffee table

■ YOU'LL HAVE BOTH a coffee table and a serving tray when you make this attractive butler's table. When you have guests, its top lifts off for serving, then fits back firmly on the leg assembly when you use it as a table. As you can see, it is a beautiful table when you do careful work, and it is a handsome addition to any home.

The trick in making this project is to use friction hinges. These hinges let you position its four leaves at any angle from horizontal to vertical to convert it to a tray with built-in handles. The

Use a plywood template to guide the router base for cutting semicircular hinge mortises

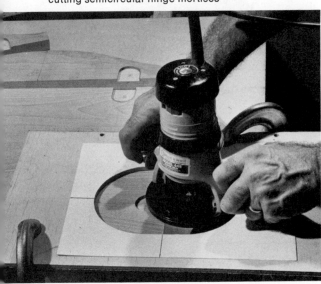

Shim the hinge mortises in the table leaves to make up for the single-thickness hinge leaf

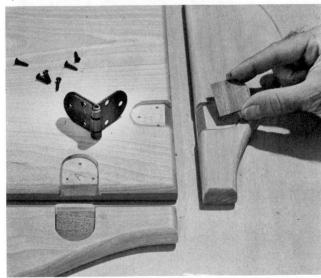

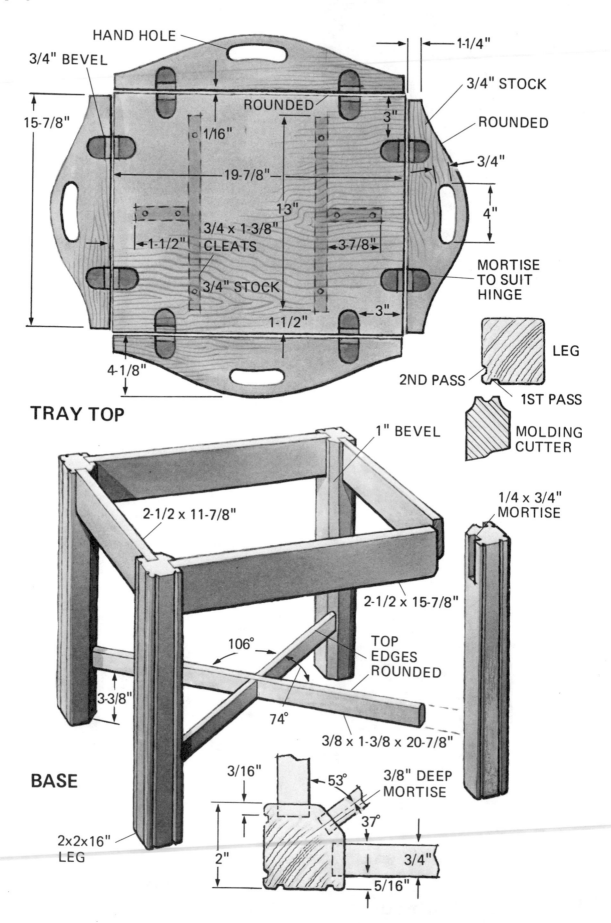

HAND HOLE

3/4" BEVEL

15-7/8"

1/16"

ROUNDED

19-7/8"

13"

3/4 x 1-3/8"
CLEATS

1-1/2"

3/4" STOCK

1-1/2"

3-7/8"

4-1/8"

TRAY TOP

1-1/4"

3/4" STOCK

ROUNDED

3/4"

3"

4"

MORTISE
TO SUIT
HINGE

LEG

2ND PASS

1ST PASS

MOLDING
CUTTER

1" BEVEL

2-1/2 x 11-7/8"

1/4 x 3/4"
MORTISE

2-1/2 x 15-7/8"

106°

3-3/8"

74°

TOP
EDGES
ROUNDED

3/8 x 1-3/8 x 20-7/8"

BASE

3/16"

53°

3/8" DEEP
MORTISE

37°

3/4"

2x2x16"
LEG

2"

5/16"

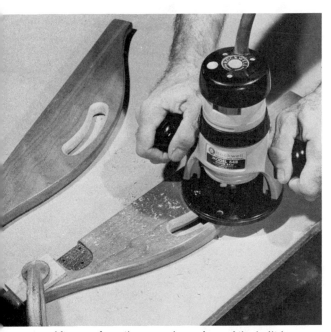

After you form the curved openings of the built-in tray handles with a ¾-in. drill bit and sabre saw, use a router to carefully round the edges

Cleats fastened to the underside of the tabletop fit inside the aprons to register the top automatically with the base when placed in the correct position

cleats on the underside cleverly position the tray/top on its four legs so it can't slide off.

You can convert these plans to just about any size table. If you buy one like it in the store it will usually be 33x44 in. I made mine smaller than this, for I found the bigger size and greater weight make it impractical for a woman to use the top as a tray.

Making this table and serving tray is not a difficult job, but neither is it a hammer-and-saw project. A router will form the semi-circular hinge mortises and round the edges. A table saw and molding cutter will form the decorative corner beading on the legs, a sabre saw will cut the tray leaves and hand grips and a drill press will form the stretcher mortises.

make all legs alike

In the drawing on the opposite page, note that all four legs are made alike; the inner corners are first beveled 45°, then mortised at the top for the aprons and 3 in. up from the bottom for the stretchers. I used my table saw to rip the leg squares from a glued-up slab consisting of three ¾ x 12 x 16-in. pieces, then dressed the four sides to 2 in. square.

Since the legs are not set in a square relationship but rather rectangular, the cross stretchers must enter the legs at a corresponding angle. To determine the correct angle for the stretcher mor-

tises, number the legs and stand them upright on a flat surface the proper distance apart. Place a straightedge diagonally across the center of the bevels of two facing legs and draw a line across the tops. Do the same with the other two legs. Now tilt your drill-press table to correspond with the cross lines on the legs and drill a series of ⅜-in. holes ⅜ in. deep in one pair of legs. Finally, do this for the others, tilting the table the other way.

now build the top

To build the top, you'll have to edge-glue several boards and join them with dowels. Each butler-table hinge has a single-thickness leaf and a double-thickness one. It's standard to rout both mortises to suit the thicker leaf, then shim under the thin leaf. A bevel will have to be hand-chiseled at the outer edge of each mortise for hinge clearance.

If your router has a 5-in.-dia. base (most do), you can make your plywood hinge-mortising template the size given; if not, cut it to suit. Use the template's centerlines to position it over the hinge locations and place cardboard between the top and tray leaf for clearance. Then hold template, plus top and leaf, with C-clamps. The eight hinges can be purchased from Armor Co., Box 290, Deer Park, New York 11729, for about $16 postpaid.

The top 20 lures to catch the lunkers

BY BUCK ROGERS and BILL MCKEOWN

Famous fisherman Buck Rogers proudly displays an Amazon tucanare. Rogers worked with the editors in naming the best baits for this article

No matter where in the world you are fishing, one of these tackle-box winners should help you bring home a genuine fish story

■ MAKING A SELECTION like this is nearly as dangerous as judging a small town's beautiful-baby contest. Someone's bound to be unhappy because we left out his favorite. There's no way to please everyone.

Our selection here, however, ought to just about guarantee good fishing results almost anywhere in the world. Our choices are based on experience stalking a wide variety of fish around the globe, plus recommendations from hundreds of other fishing authorities.

bass specials

We have a special category for these two lures because the large-mouth is the most popular game fish in the United States. Sooner or later every angler will get acquainted with this species.

• *Plastic worm:* Since the dawn of angling history, the night crawler has been the most effective bait a fisherman could string on a hook. It was only a question of time before someone brought out an artificial worm, and Nick Creme did so in 1949. Since then, the plastic worm has become No. 1 bass lure. Most bass fishermen use it more than all others combined; many fish nothing else. Today, rigged and unrigged worms are made by a number of reputable companies. To prepare your own, impale a 5/0 hook in an eight-inch worm, bring the barb out ½ inch behind the head and draw the worm up around the hook's shank. Most anglers turn the barb and bury it in the worm to make it weedless. For casting weight, attach a bullet-shaped slip sinker to the leader.

When fishing, cast the worm out and let it set-tle to the bottom. With your rod tip high, reel in slowly and crawl the worm back over the bottom. When a bass picks it up, strike. If you miss repeatedly, use a delayed strike. Experiment. Worm fishing is a science that takes practice.

• *Spinnerbait:* Another hot bass lure is a safety-pin device with lead body, hook and skirt on one wire and one or more spinner blades on the other. This weedless lure can be fished through heavy cover. Some anglers buzz it across shallows with the blade raising a water hump. Others work it over the bottom like a plastic worm. This relatively new bait, made by several firms, has earned a spot in most professional bassers' tackle boxes. The one we have selected for our photo of life-size lures is the Bass Hog by Storm Manufacturing of Norman, Okla.

topside teasers

The greatest thrill of angling is the surface strike. We always start with surface lures and only reluctantly change to underwater performers. Our three surface selections are an unbeatable combination; each is a great lure in its own right.

• *Chugger:* We're not sure that this lure was in James Heddon's collection when he started the company in 1900, but it certainly gained fame shortly thereafter. This is a popper-type lure which does nothing on straight retrieve but performs a variety of tricks in the hands of an experienced angler. Chug it in water-scooping surface explosions, wiggle it gently in one place, make it "walk the dog" in the frantic manner of an escaping fish.

• *Jitterbug:* Made by the Fred Arbogast Co. of Akron, Ohio, this could be the most popular surface lure in angling history. Retrieved in a normal manner, it slowly crawls across the surface, gurgling and flinging spray. Worked as a surface popper, it responds to rod tip action like something alive. It takes bass, is one of the better surface lures for pike, and the smaller models are deadly for big trout at night. To take big bass in midsummer, go Jitterbugging in the shallows of your local lake late at night with the black ⅝-ounce model.

• *Injured Minnow:* This famous lure with propellers fore and aft is made by Creek Chub Bait Co. of Garrett, Ind. Extremely versatile, it works well when the water is calm, and on a wind or rain-ruffled surface it's probably the best surface lure we know. It's a quality bait made of wood in various sizes, colors, finishes. Fish it along weed beds for bass and pike. Let it sit awhile before the retrieve—then brace for an explosion.

the spoon group

No collection would be complete without these two fine spoons. They compete with other lures under normal conditions and also perform special services that the others can't match.

• *Dardevle:* Easily the most famous of fishing spoons, this old standby is made by the Lou J. Eppinger Co. of Dearborn, Mich. The red and white standard Dardevle, designed for muskie, pike and walleye, is a northwoods must. A fine casting lure, its tantalizing slow wobble makes it an ideal trolling lure also. But if we had to choose just one spoon, the Eppinger Copy Cat would have to be it. This hump-backed Dardevle operates at higher speeds, takes snook, tarpon, trout, bass and other fish as readily as pike and walleye. (Buck prefers the ⅜ ounce, and is never without a half dozen.)

• *Silver Minnow:* As for weeds, this is the lure. Made by the Louis Johnson Co. of Highland Park, Ill., it started the story about the angler who made lures from his wife's teaspoons. Fish this streamlined silver spoon with a pork rind strip as far back in the brush as you can heave it. It's deadly for southern bass, pike, muskie or any game fish in heavy cover; add an eight-inch worm for deep water.

deep and slow

Most lunkers are lazy. They let small energetic fish chase faster prey and wait for easy meals to pass their lairs. For them you need deep-running, wobbling lures.

• *Flatfish:* This gang-hook creation, developed by the Helin Tackle Co. of Detroit in 1933, has been a favorite ever since. Its wobbling action cuts an eight-inch swath through the water and drives deep walleyes wild. Most people don't know the Flatfish is the most popular trout lure in South America. Called a "caiman" there, it annually takes more giant Andes trout than all other lures or flies combined. For trolling, not casting, it's fished with the line tied to the lure and a weight a foot ahead. A favorite is the U-20 in orange.

• *Lazy Ike:* Extremely versatile underwater, the Lazy Ike was developed by Kautsky Sporting Goods in the early '40s and is now made by Lazy Ike Corp., Fort Dodge, Iowa. This lure takes everything. We troll it for deep bass in winter and spring, and it's a first choice for northern small-mouth and walleye. Try it for open-water pike and muskie, through a stream riffle for small-mouth or big trout. Fishing the Amazon, a friend trailed one beside our dugout canoe and took a wild six-foot surubi catfish. Tops for trolling, you can also cast floater models back into the shallows.

• *Bomber:* This is the original "crank bait." Made by Bomber Bait Co., Gainesville, Tex., it has been dredging bottoms of southern impoundments for over 25 years and catching lots of bass. Fish sloping banks with floaters, deeper points with others. To bring 'em out of the deep, add a slip sinker up front. Although a largemouth lure, the Bomber is also excellent for walleye, small-mouth, muskie, pike off deep points, big trout and more. All the many colors and finishes take fish.

big and deadly

• *Rapala:* A slim-bodied Finnish creation distributed in North America by the Normark Corp. of Minneapolis, it's one of the great all-time fishing lures. When this balsa import appeared on the U.S. scene in 1962, it created a revolution. Bass, muskie, pike, trout, walleye, panfish all fell for it. Fishermen bought out the complete stocks of tackle shops and caught fish with wild abandon. Today the furor is over, but the Rapala in eight models and dozens of colors remains a great one. Several should be in your tackle box.

• *Rebel:* Topnotch U.S. contender for honors the Rapala debut started, this fine one from Plastic Research & Development Corp., Fort Smith, Ark., is durable and deadly. Work floating models like surface lures or retrieve just under the surface. Sinkers and deep runners are equally effective. On one lake, Rebel took more trout one season than all other lures combined. Another time it proved most deadly of all peacock bass lures. Use it for bass, pike, muskie, all game fish—it's great.

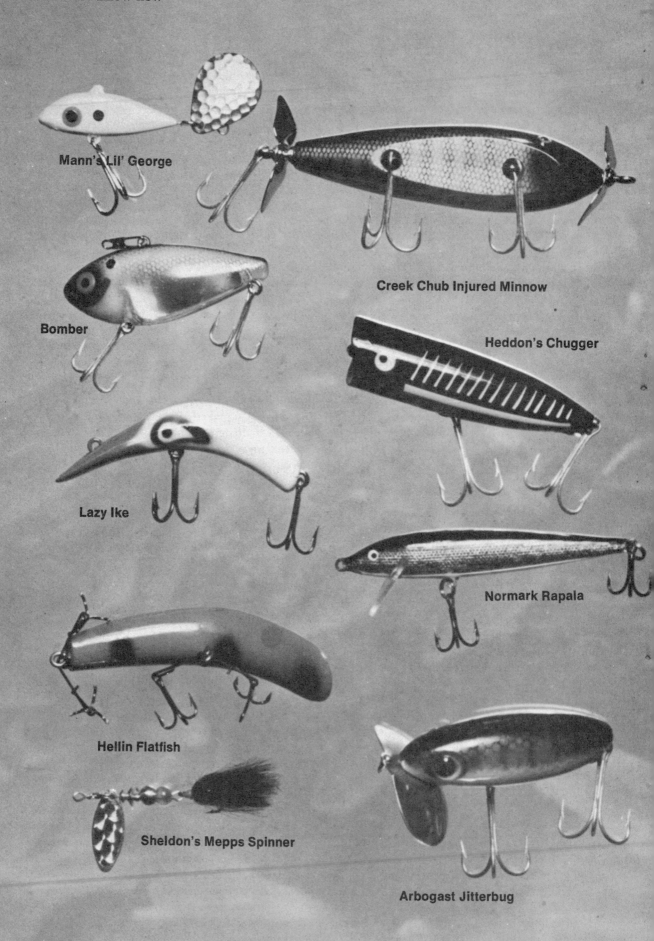

Mann's Lil' George

Creek Chub Injured Minnow

Bomber

Heddon's Chugger

Lazy Ike

Normark Rapala

Hellin Flatfish

Sheldon's Mepps Spinner

Arbogast Jitterbug

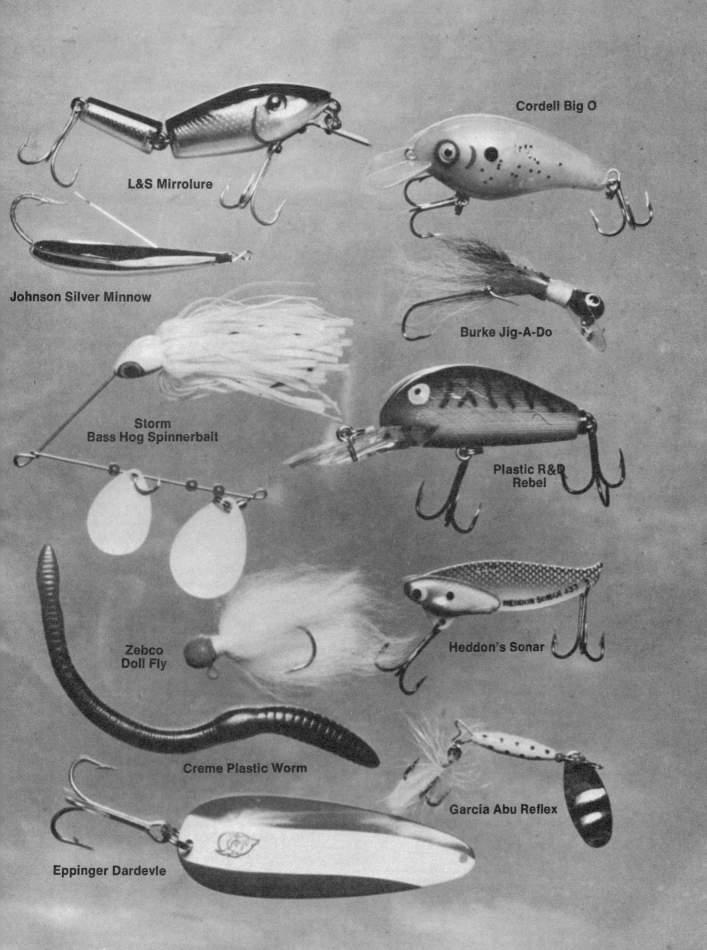

L&S Mirrolure

Cordell Big O

Johnson Silver Minnow

Burke Jig-A-Do

Storm
Bass Hog Spinnerbait

Plastic R&D
Rebel

Zebco
Doll Fly

Heddon's Sonar

Creme Plastic Worm

Garcia Abu Reflex

Eppinger Dardevle

• *Big O:* When a hand-carved balsa model of this fat plug won a bass tournament a couple years ago, it became the hottest of lures and earned its place on this elite list. Manufactured by Cordell Tackle Co., Hot Springs, Ark., it now comes in four sizes, many colors. In Ontario we've had smallmouth bass eat it up, but also once caught more muskies on this fatso than on a dozen previous trips. And in the Amazon jungle, big dorado and peacock bass tear into our Big O. It's a winner.

the fast ones

Sometimes fish pass up old favorites, yawn at worms and jigs. Occasionally it takes a fast lure to trigger these lethargic ones into action.

• *Sonar:* This glittering metallic mover made by James Heddon's Sons of Dowagiac, Mich., is a forward-weighted lure with a fast sound-producing wiggle that casts like a lead weight and can be fished at almost any depth. Each of three holes for the line produces a different action that's great for largemouth and stream-bred smallmouth alike. Smaller Sonars are hot for trout, and ever since this lure was introduced there have been dozens of imitations. None, though, have surpassed it.

• *Mirrolure:* "Best jerk bait ever made," is how veteran snook fishermen describe this one from the L & S Bait Co. of Bradley, Ill. For a fast-moving lure for fresh or saltwater, this shiny sardine brings out the worst in game fish. Some strike it from hunger; others for spite when you give it little jerks with your rod and it darts like frightened bait. Choose from many colors and finishes for all inshore saltwater species, schooling bass, fast water trout.

spinning lures

They do these well in Europe; one of these spinner favorites comes from Sweden, the other from France. Both rate top tackle-box billing.

• *Abu Reflex Spinner:* Made by Abu of Sweden and distributed by Garcia of Teaneck, N. J., this one comes from two of the quality names in the business, and performs like it. A favorite for big Irish pike and Norwegian salmon, it also took a 17-pound brown trout recently to win the Abu G.B. International Contest. Over here it takes all types of trout, is effective for pike and largemouth, has a wide range of casting and spinning sizes, blade and body colors.

• *Mepps Spinner:* When spinning was introduced here in the 1940s, this French spinning lure came along. Today, distributed by Sheldon's, Inc. of Antigo, Wis., it's known coast to coast as one of the finest trout lures. It's used as well for far north grayling, white water walleye, white bass, crappie, black bass, you name it. Keep the blade wet and moving.

bottom bumpers

"If they're not on top, they're on the bottom," is the old adage; this lure group goes down and gets 'em.

• *Doll Fly:* One of the world's best known jigs, this teaser from the Zebco Doll Div. of the Brunswick Corp., Tulsa, Okla., will take bass off the bottom of impoundments or haul snapper up from southern seas. Use it for lake trout, salmon, walleye, crappie. Fish it slow or crank as fast as you can through schooling, feeding gamesters. You can cast the jig a country mile with any rig. It gets to the bottom fast, and you can bump it along with minimum risk of snagging. Doll Fly comes in many sizes: yellow and white are favorite colors.

• *Jig-A-Doo:* Made by Burke Flexo-Products Co., Traverse City, Mich. this little tantalizer is a cross between a jig and an underwater action lure. Its plastic lip gives it a wiggle that needs no help from the angler. A trailer hook attached to the main hook makes it even more effective in nailing short strikes. Considered among the best lures for walleye and smallmouth. One once was taken away from the bass we were fishing for by three muskies. It works on the bonefish flats, murders surf-feeding snook, and is equally effective for tarpon. If there's a lure which can do almost everything, this little Jig-A-Doo might be it.

• *Lil' George:* This heavy little spinner, made by Mann's Bait Co., Eufaula, Ala., is relatively new compared to most of our other selections, but has already made quite a name for itself among professional bass fishermen. It casts like a sinker, hits bottom faster than you can catch your breath and frequently induces strikes on the way down. You can jig it, bounce it down a rocky ledge, buzz it past a brush pile, work it in a swift current which will ruin the action of most other lures. It's a great bass lure that is also equally effective for walleye and white bass. Recently we fed some to northern pike and created a mild revolution in a certain northwoods fishing lodge. We introduced Lil' George to half a dozen species of South American fish and again it was love at first sight. When things are tough, you're still not whipped. Send Lil' George.

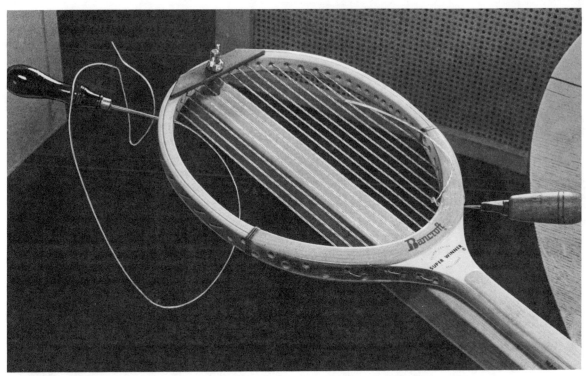

Simple jig for holding racket is length of wood and clamps, turns table into rig for racket repairs

Restring your own tennis racket

BY ELMER K. NORTON

Using these simple techniques and tips, and a little practice you can save playing time—and money. You'll be pleased at what surprisingly good results this system gives. Use it on badminton rackets, too

■ IT'S SATURDAY MORNING and during a warm-up rally you pop a string on your favorite racket. No need to give up the weekend matches or play with an uncomfortable borrowed racket. If your restringing and repair shop is closed or miles away, try some of these simple shortcuts I've developed over 25 years.

Less than $12 can provide you with a jig to hold the racket and materials for restringing and replacing your grip as well. Sending your racket out for restringing alone might cost you $10 to $13 in nylon, $20 to $24 in gut. A professional restringing machine can cost over $400.

Materials you will need for the method shown here are simply a three-foot length of 1½ x 1½ stock, preferably hardwood, an eight-inch length of 1½-inch dowel (like that on which rugs are sometimes delivered) that you will cushion with

a wrap of leather or adhesive tape. Also two three-inch or four-inch "C" clamps to hold the wood base and your racket to your workbench or kitchen table plus a four-inch ⅜-16 NC hold-down bolt with wingnut to secure the head of the racket, and some scraps of hardwood so the clamps don't scratch your racket handle. A couple of awls from a hardware store will hold the string in place.

I recommend nylon string in a 35-foot length from your tennis shop or mail-order supplier, at about $4.50 or $5, for your 18 main and 20 cross strings. Nylon lasts several times longer than gut and is much easier to work with. Mail-order sources include The Tennis Center, 68 Harrison Ave., Congers, N.Y. 10920, and Tennis Accessories, 616 Schreiber Ave., Coplay, Pa. 18037.

Clamp down your racket, as shown, with the

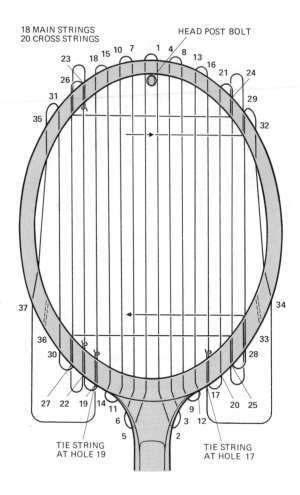

18 MAIN STRINGS
20 CROSS STRINGS

HEAD POST BOLT

TIE STRING
AT HOLE 19

TIE STRING
AT HOLE 17

restring your racket, continued

tighten, and insert the awl in hole 4. Repeat this procedure on the other side through holes 5, 6, 7. Awls are now in holes 4 and 7.

Continue this threading and tightening process alternately in numerical order, as shown, until there are 16 strings threaded and awls are in holes 29 and 31. Strumming each string as it is tightened will give you an indication of proper tension. Thread 32 and 34, then 35 and 37, being careful to skip holes 33 and 36. Pull strings extra tight, insert awls, rethread those loose ends through holes 17 and 19, and tie off each with a simple half hitch. If the nylon is slippery, add an extra half hitch; then cut off excess string ¼-inch from the knot.

threading the cross strings

Cross strings are threaded from the remaining 16-foot length. If hole 22 is a top hole, thread one end up through and half hitch to the main string there. If a bottom hole, No. 20 on the other side must be used instead. Thread the other end through hole 27 and weave under and over the main vertical strings over to and through hole 25 on the opposite side. Tighten, insert awl and continue weaving across and up the racket until 20 cross strings have been strung. The 20th string goes through hole 26, is tightened, threaded through hole 23 and then tied to the main string there and cut off. During cross-string threading when a main string already occupies a hole, it's helpful to sharpen the tip of the cross string; snip it off diagonally to a point.

Now go over the racket with a slim dowel or pencil (since your awl might cut into a string) and straighten those strings out of line so that they all cross at right angles and are parallel.

Grip replacement is also not too difficult—once you know how. A good quality leather grip, about 3½ feet long, is approximately $3 from a sporting goods store or tennis shop. Remove the old grip, and coat the handle with mucilage or shellac. Air until tacky. With a ⅜-inch flat-headed nail, secure the tapered end of the grip strip flush with the butt end of the handle, nailing through ¼ inch from the end of the leather. Hold the racket head between your legs and wrap the grip flush around the butt end and then on down the handle clockwise with the leather layers butting or slightly overlapping, if so designed. Tack the finished end with a ⅜-inch nail, trim off excess leather with a razor, and cover the nail and edge with two or three turns of ½-inch plastic tape.

Gut restringing can be attempted after you have become proficient with nylon. Because of gut's

side grooves slanting down and toward the head of the racket. All strings always go into the lower hole and out the upper hole of the groove. Starting with the main strings, the vertical ones, cut a 19-foot length of nylon and thread through the two top holes so that half (9½ feet) goes on each side of the center-post bolt holding the racket head. The bolt is filed flat on each side to protect strings from damage. Thread these main strings down through the first holes on each side of the neck.

Sight through these holes to see their direction and then carefully but firmly insert one awl into No. 1 to hold the string in place. Wrap the string coming out hole No. 2 one and a half turns around the string-tightening dowel handle and, using the frame for leverage, turn to tension the string. Be sure the string coming out is straight so you are not tightening against added friction. Insert the second awl in hole No. 2 and remove the tightening handle. Thread the string through holes 3 and 4,

reaction to moisture (a rain shower can ruin its tension), it should be treated with preservative after stringing and occasionally during active use after exposure to damp conditions or when the strings are becoming slightly frayed.

Mix one part of white three-pound cut absolute shellac with five parts of water-free ethanol in an 8-ounce salad dressing jar with screw top. Store a ¾-inch brush with cutdown handle inside the jar. When strings are frayed or damp, first dry with talc or a fluffy towel, then paint on a light coat. Thin mixture with alcohol from time to time. Too thick a coat or too frequent use makes gut strings lose resiliency. Never use it on any type of nylon strings.

The stringing method outlined here can also be used with all metal rackets except the Wilson Steel and Seamco Aluminum. The rig works as well with squash, paddle and badminton rackets, although badminton strings are 19-gauge and much thinner.

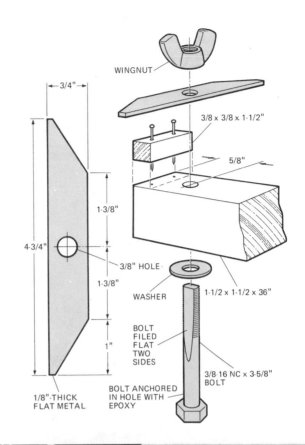

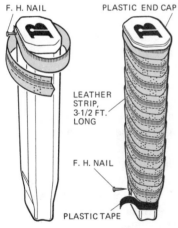

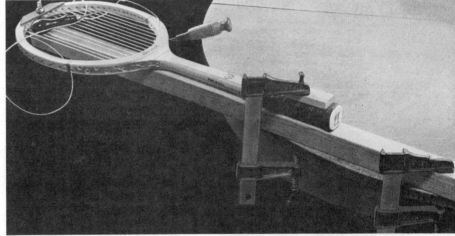

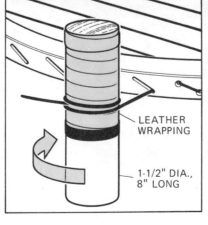

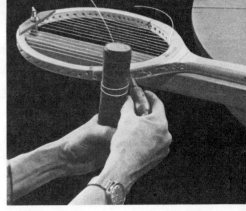

Racket jig uses bolt cap (at upper right) to hold the head of racket plus C-clamps to secure a brace to the table. Renewing grip (above) starts with a leather strip 3½ feet long which is stretch-wrapped down the handle and finally secured with a nail and a plastic tape ring

Tensioning of new strings (right) is done with a 1½-inch-thick dowel with leather or adhesive wrap. The string is looped around the handle and is turned to tighten, held with an awl while the next length is laced in place. Cross strings weave under and over the main strings

How to get in shape

BY JACK GALUB

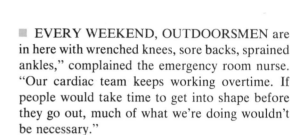

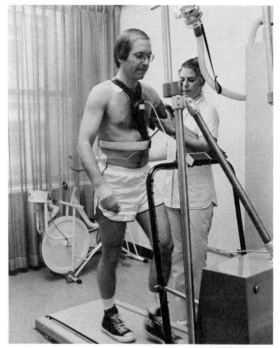

The stress test is uphill work as the treadmill's angle is increased. Charles Perschetz, of Cardio-Metrics, demonstrates during an EKG

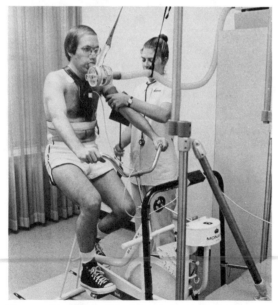

The aerobic ability of the blood to feed oxygen to the muscles is studied with this breathing apparatus during a bicycle exercising exam

■ EVERY WEEKEND, OUTDOORSMEN are in here with wrenched knees, sore backs, sprained ankles," complained the emergency room nurse. "Our cardiac team keeps working overtime. If people would take time to get into shape before they go out, much of what we're doing wouldn't be necessary."

But this year can be different. By starting a training program now, you can be in good enough condition to cut down the chance of becoming another hospital statistic.

Conditioning for the field has three key targets: improved cardiovascular fitness, increased flexibility and agility, and specific muscle strength. Sounds complicated? Some 60 years of fitness medical research show that if you're now in fairly good shape you can start rounding into condition at the end of a month or so. If you've grown fat and flabby, you may need six to eight weeks.

Stamina—that ability to hike 10 miles or more without feeling completely exhausted—depends on your heart and your respiratory system's ability to supply oxygen to the more than 600 muscles in your body, particularly when you are back-packing up a hill or heading into the wind. Fortunately, the heart is an endurance muscle. The more regularly it is exercised with fast walking, jogging, bicycling or swimming, the better it works under stress. Hearts that aren't adapted to regular exercise peak out too quickly. Like a detuned car engine, they can develop an irregular rhythm. Sometimes they grind to a halt.

The most effective way to check your cardiovascular system today is the stress test. You ride a special stationary bicycle or climb an electrically driven treadmill that can be tilted into an ever-steepening hill. Your heart's reaction is recorded on electrocardiograph (EKG) tape and monitored by a cardiologist on an oscilloscope. You'll also breathe into an electronic apparatus that

New medical research shows a physical checkup
plus some simple exercises can change outdoor
sport from an endurance test into healthy fun

determines your body's ability to feed oxygen to your muscles. The stress test may also detect heart problems which could cause sudden death unless treated. These tests are now given in some hospital exercise centers or by such licensed groups as Cardio-Metrics, Inc., New York City, which specialize in the testing and prescription of conditioning programs for cardiacs and noncardiacs alike.

Interval training, a sophisticated walk-jog formula, is usually prescribed to ease an outdoorsman into a conditioning program. Each session is divided into warm-up, stimulus, cool down, with the stimulus making the heart work to build up fitness. Extensive research indicates that 75 to 85 percent of your age-related maximum heart rate (see table) must be reached for a planned length of time for cardiovascular improvement. During your sessions, you monitor your pulse regularly for five seconds (and then multiply by 12 for pulse rate) to make sure you are not overworking or underworking your heart.

If there are no testing facilities near you—and an exam by your doctor assures you of a good cardiac profile—you can develop your own shaping-up program. If your profile is poor—a history of heart disease in your family, high blood pressure, overweight, too much smoking—a complete physical checkup and consultation with your doctor is essential before you start.

Begin easily—you're not out for the Olympics or your local ball club. Jogging takes a slow short stride, done from the heels forward rather than on the balls of the feet. First try jogging 50 paces and walking 50 for 10 or 15 minutes. As your wind builds up, you can walk less. You may find yourself slow-jogging a quarter mile in two weeks, half a mile in a month. With no park or track nearby, you can jog around the block or from room to room at home.

For the flexibility and agility you'll need while hiking and climbing, practice walking on the outsides of your feet and then the insides with your ankles turned in. These exercises are awkward and difficult at first, but a few minutes every other day will stretch and strengthen muscles, tendons and ligaments.

Next, imitate a basketball guard or boxer with feet apart, knees slightly bent. Bob, weave and pivot on the balls of your feet, followed by jumps several inches off the floor. For the lower back and hip joints you will use canoeing and climbing, bend your knees until you can put your palms on the floor. Then try straightening your legs while pulling in your abdominal muscles. Two or three stomach contractions held for five to 10 seconds are enough for each exercise session.

Push-ups should be added to your every-other-day routine. Starting flat on the floor, push up to full arm extension and then lower with body straight until your chest touches the floor. Most people at first aren't able to do more than one or two properly without cheating by bending the body.

MAXIMUM WORK RATE

For training to be most effective, a workout pulse rate at 75 to 85 percent of maximum efficient heartbeat is recommended. But moderation is vital: Check with your doctor and ease into training.

Age	Maximum pulse/heart rate	85%
20	200	170
22	198	168
24	196	166
26	194	164
28	192	163
30	190	161
32	189	160
34	187	158
36	186	158
38	184	156
40	182	154
45	179	152
50	175	148
55	171	145

turn the page

Travel tote for rod and gun

You can safeguard your hunting and fishing gear with this custom case. Here's how to make it yourself from PVC for under $25

BY BOB STEARNS

A custom case of PVC can protect one rod in the two-inch diameter size or nearly 20 in a six-inch width. One end cap is cemented on permanently and the other is secured with a cable and padlock. The handle balances the case

■ WHAT COULD SPOIL a trip faster than to arrive at some remote hunting or fishing hot spot and find your favorite rod or gun has been damaged along the way? A usable replacement might be impossible to locate.

Yet you can make your own custom-fitted *lockable* case for about $25 or less. It's a small price to protect the valuable equipment you'll be carrying inside it.

Basic material of this easy-to-build tote is PVC pipe, an amazingly tough product used by the plumbing trade. It is readily available in many diameters and in lengths up to 20 feet. It also comes in a variety of wall thicknesses but the lightest, called "schedule 40," is more than sufficient. It's almost ¼-inch thick, and you can stand on it without hurting it. The length you choose will depend on the longest item you plan to trans-

port, but keep in mind that some airlines may balk at containers over eight feet long as baggage.

PVC is sold by its inside diameter. If you plan to take a small rifle or shotgun, you might get by with five-inch diameter. Larger guns will need six-inch pipe. If only rods are carried, a size down to two inches will work well. To help you select, here is a schedule 40 chart with approximate costs and weights:

Diameter (in.)	Approximate Weight (lbs. per ft.)	Approximate Price (per ft.)	End Cap Price (each)
2	0.83	$ .67	$ .78
3	1.50	1.40	1.79
4	2.17	2.00	4.28
5	3.00	2.70	5.68
6	3.67	3.50	6.62

Most retail plumbing supply houses carry PVC. Use slip-on caps, not threaded ones. Prices may have risen since this writing.

Besides the pipe and two caps, you need a small container of PVC cement, rubber cement, one foot of ⅛ to 3/16-inch steel cable, two brass sleeves to fit the cable, two adjustable stainless-steel hose clamps to fit around the pipe, a sturdy handle, heavy-duty eye strap and small padlock.

Assembly is easy. Try caps on both ends of PVC for the loosest fit. Rubber cement a circle of ½-inch or thicker foam plastic padding inside the tighter fitting cap and follow instructions on the PVC cement can to glue cap permanently on pipe.

With a small knife and very fine sandpaper, bevel the outside edge of the other end of the pipe and smooth inside the cap for an easy slip-fit. Make a small loop in one end of the steel cable, and secure it by slipping on a sleeve and hammering flat. Drill a hole slightly larger than the cable in the center of the removable cap. Feed free end of the cable through this hole and secure it inside with the other sleeve. With padlock hooked through the loop end of the cable and eye strap, the position to bolt the eye strap is determined.

Once the eye strap is bolted so the tight cable holds the cap in place, file down slots in bolts so a screwdriver can no longer get a bite to remove them.

Next, bolt an inexpensive but sturdy handle to the inside of the hose clamps, as shown in the photo. This provides a grip than can be loosened for moving along the length of the pipe to a place that is at the center of balance for every load.

When both gun and fishing rods are to be carried in the case, a piece of ¼-inch plywood can be cut to fit the full length of the tube as a divider. Guns and rods should be kept in protective bags or wrapped with old towels and bundled tightly with masking tape, if necessary, to prevent rattling, movement or chafing.

The number of rods that can be carried is surprising. Unless you have spinning rods with very large guides, you can get up to four rods in a two-inch pipe case, a dozen in a four-inch tube, and eight or ten plus a shotgun in the six-incher.

And does the system work? My five-inch case has hauled 18 rods all over Africa and Central America, plus a lot of other places. I have yet to have a single guide get bent.

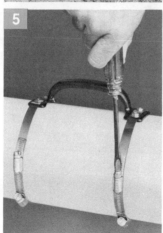
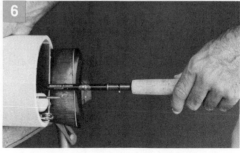

(1) Cement foam padding into bottom cap. The cable (2) holding the top cap has a brass sleeve hammered on to form a loop which padlocks to the eye strap (3). The screwheads are filed so they can't be removed. The cable is kept short so that the top cap (4) won't slide off. Adjustable hose clamps (5) hold the handle to balance the load. A divider (6) separates the guns and rods

Need a sink? The Brooks Porta Sink (photo below) holds the three trays that you will need for your portable darkroom

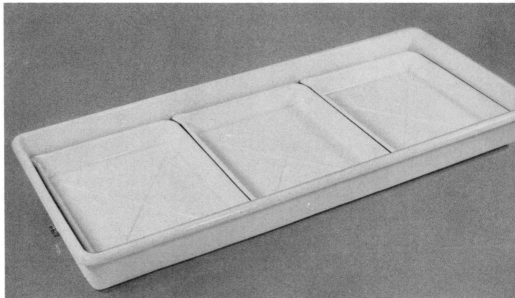

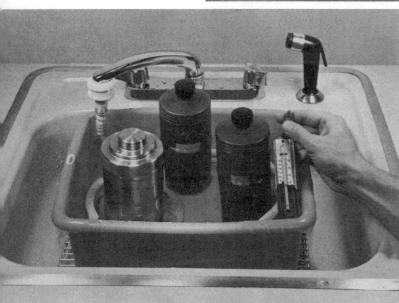

Temporary darkroom tactics include the use of a plastic basin or dishpan as a carryall to carry each night's equipment to your workroom. It can also be used as a temperature-control bath (as shown above) and finally as a washer

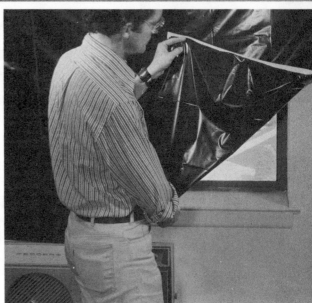

The windows can be darkened with plastic lawn bags. It is suggested that the black plastic bags be used for daylight processing but the red-brown type will be satisfactory for nighttime developing work

Borrow space for a darkroom

BY ELBERT LAWTON

Have you had trouble finding enough space
in your home or apartment for a permanent darkroom?
Here are some suggestions to help you purchase
the proper equipment and set up a work plan for
a portable darkroom which can be
used almost anywhere

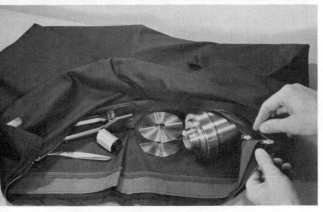

The Tray-Rak (top) holds three trays, step-fashion and costs from $11 to about $16. The lower photo shows how a changing bag can be used for loading film-developing tanks of many different sizes

■ IN MOST HOMES, finding space for a permanent darkroom is very difficult. When faced with this situation, many photographers find it easier to borrow space somewhere around the house for a few hours. One of the problems they encounter is that they are losing half their time setting up and taking down all the equipment which is necessary for developing and printing. If this is a problem you face, portable darkroom equipment and a work plan are what you need.

The first rule is to keep everything as simple as possible. Buy and use only the essentials—"time-saving" luxuries will seem a lot less luxurious if the time saved is then spent in moving them from place to place. Some photographers fear that using just the essentials will mean they

turn the page

can't do as good a job as the guy with a permanent setup. This isn't true! However, it does mean that you can't count on quite as many prints per evening without cutting quality.

The second rule is to compartmentalize your work. This will involve careful planning as it simply isn't practical to drag out and set up *everything* each time you have a free hour or two to work.

It's better to break your darkroom work down into separate stages. Each of these stages can then be served by its own equipment and supplies. I divide my darkroom work into four such stages: chemical mixing; film processing; printing and print processing; and print drying, spotting and mounting. Limit yourself to one stage per work session (with the possible exception of the mixing stage). By using a method such as this you will find you accomplish a lot more than if you try to do everything at once.

mixing the chemicals

Chemical preparation takes little space and can be done in full room light. You can usually mix your chemicals the night you plan to use them, especially if you go to pre-mixed or liquid chemicals. Many powdered chemicals are supposed to be mixed at temperatures much higher than the standard 68°F. processing temperature. Mix them before dinner, and they'll be down to room temperature by the time you're ready for work.

You have the choice of the one-shot developers that are discarded after use or the kind you replenish. I prefer the one-shot developers as they're fresh each time—important when you do only occasional darkroom work.

Your equipment for this stage should include a quart graduate for measuring and mixing, a two-ounce graduate for adding replenisher (if you use it), a long-stem bar mixing spoon or mixing paddle, a funnel, a thermometer and plastic bottles. Some chemicals, which age more slowly (such as fixer and hypo eliminator), can be mixed more economically and conveniently in gallon quantities. This is especially true of fixer, which goes fast. If you do mix a gallon, divide it into quart bottles—the chemicals in the unopened bottles will last even longer, and you'll have less weight to lug around. If you can, always use separate graduates and paddles for mixing devel-

oper and fixer; otherwise, wash extra carefully between chemicals to keep one from contaminating the other.

Probably the best place in the house to do your mixing is the kitchen sink. And to carry your chemicals and equipment from storage to the sink and back, use a plastic dishpan—it will come in handy again in the next stage.

Now you are ready to do the actual developing. Developing film requires just a little additional equipment: a daylight-type developing tank, film reels, a changing bag, scissors, a length of hose (optional) from a bathroom hair-sprayer attachment, and (if you use 35-mm film) either a cassette opener or bottle-cap opener. The basic chemicals you'll need are film developer, stop bath (optional) and fixer. To speed up your processing, you can use rapid fixer instead of regular "hypo" type and a hypo neutralizer between fixing and washing to reduce washing time. Dip your film in wetting agent to speed up drying a bit and reduce the formation of water spots on the film.

Use a changing bag as a "dark-room." You will find that it is just big enough to hold the film, tank and reels. You can load the tank at your convenience.

plastic dishpan is useful

When developing, your plastic dishpan can serve double duty as a carry-all to bring your paraphernalia to the kitchen sink and as a water jacket. Filled with water at 68°F., it will bring all the chemicals and the tank to the correct temperature and hold them there for a period of time.

The best way to wash the film is to use a faucet's attached hose to direct a strong jet of water (still at 68°) through the center of the reels down to the bottom of the tank, where it will flush any impurities away. Some tanks come with hose assemblies, but with a little tinkering I have found that the hair-spray hose mentioned earlier seems to work well with many different kinds of tanks.

Printing takes a bit more equipment. You will need a developer and stop-bath tray at least as big as the largest prints you'll make as well as a larger tray for the fixing bath. You will also need tongs to agitate prints and carry them from one tray to another, and finally another deep plastic basin drilled with holes to serve as a washer.

Of course, you'll also need an enlarger and lenses for it. Unless you're sure you'll be shooting just 35-mm or 126 Instamatic photos for the rest of your life, it pays to buy the 35-mm-to-120 size—it won't be much more expensive. Look for one that can be disassembled easily for compact storage, but that is still of quality construction. The quality of your enlarger will directly affect the quality of your prints. If you want to get good sharp prints, buy a well-built enlarger. This is no place to save money.

You'll need enlarging lenses, too. You should get a 2-inch lens for 35-mm, or a 3-inch lens for 120 negatives. If you're trying to print both sizes but can only afford one lens at first, use a 3-inch lens, and attach a close-up lens to its front when you need bigger enlargements.

In enlarging easels, your best bet is the kind with calibrated, adjustable masking bands that let you use different paper sizes or crop your borders to precisely match the shape of your image. Most photographers agree that not all photos look best in precise 8x10 proportions. Look for an easel whose masking bands are supported on all four sides, not flopping in the air when you raise them to insert the paper. You should begin with an 8x10-size easel. Even after making bigger enlargements, you'll probably find that this size is easier to use when working with smaller prints.

do without some "nonessentials"

The only essential accessory left is a safelight. If you were setting up a permanent darkroom you would surely want to include such things as enlarging timers, paper safes and focusing magnifiers. But with your portable darkroom, you can do without them at first. Count seconds aloud (say "one-hippopotamus, two-hippopotamus . . ." to space the seconds properly) or watch the kitchen clock's sweep second hand. You can remove the paper sheets one at a time from the box, placing your body as a shield between the open box and the safelight. The focus can be checked with a conventional magnifier.

Once you have all your printing equipment ready, you are faced with the question of where and how you should set it up. For the "where" you have several choices: A basement location near the utility sink will minimize disruption of your family's life, provided the location is comfortable and free of dust. The kitchen is the next best bet because of its deep sink and its countertop space—but you'll have to wait till the dishes are washed, and teach everyone to knock before coming in. The bathroom is least preferable, since its sink is too small, its tub too low, and you'll frequently have to stop to admit other family members.

A sink isn't really needed till the final wash, though, so you can set up in a dry room—pick one with lots of space, few windows and low family traffic—just by adding another dishpan full of water to hold the prints till you can take a batch of them outside for washing.

Whatever room you pick, make sure it has a sturdy table or counter that won't shake under your enlarger. Keep your "dry" operations (enlarging and paper storage) separate from wet ones (developing, stop bath and fixing), either on opposite sides of the room or with a partition between them.

All that's left is darkness—and you need that only for enlarging. For daylight processing, cover the windows with large, black plastic trash bags from the supermarket, the red-brown type will do for use at night.

It is very important that the entire room be light-tight. If the room has a door, make it light-tight with weatherstripping. If not, cover the open doorway with more plastic, overlapping and taping the bags together. Carefully look to make sure there is no other light leaking into the room. At this point, ventilation can be a problem. My kitchen fan handles the problem for me.

Print drying can be left to the day after your printing session. It won't hurt the prints to soak, though the water should be changed a few times. Squeeze an electric print-dryer into your budget if at all possible—it's the only way to make sure that the prints you've spent hours making will look as good when dry as they did wet. For matte prints, you'll get a far more smoothly finished, wrinkle-free surface than you could with a blotter; and with ferrotype tins, you'll get good glossy prints much faster than you would with plain air drying. The best size for your dryer of ferrotype tins is 16x20 inches. It's big enough to handle big prints and will let you dry four 8x10s at once.

the finishing touches

For finishing touches, take the extra steps of spotting and mounting your prints. With just three bottles of spotting tone (in different densities) and a fine brush, you can render many dust spots and other imperfections invisible. For print-mounting, your best bet is to use one of the special adhesives sold in photo stores. Electric dry-mounting presses are bulky and expensive, and though a few hobbyists dry-mount successfully with a clothes iron, there's risk of damage to the print.

Useful mounting tools include a wallboard knife, a steel straightedge for trimming, and a board with a weight on top to press the paper down for a blemish-free surface.

10 SECONDS

f/4.5

f/5.6

f/8

15 SECONDS AT f/11

f/11

12½ SEC

15 SEC

17½ SEC

f/16

Grid-squares, unlike conventional test strips, show same area of picture each time. The first test series (top to bottom, left) showed 10 seconds at f/11 to be almost right. The second series (left to right, above) showed best exposure was 15 seconds at f/11

Grid on easel (opposite page, left) shows you where to set paper squares to match position each time. Fanning squares like a card hand (right) develops them alike

Grid-square exposure tests

BY ELDON AND PEGGY HAUCK

■ THE USUAL WAY to find the right exposure in enlarging is "test-stripping." This process involves exposing each section of the print a different length of time to see which works best, but the trouble with test-stripping is that each strip covers not just a different exposure, but a different part of the subject, too. The grid-test method explained below and in the accompanying photos doesn't have that problem—and it's quicker than the tedious task of test-stripping to get the correct exposure.

First, paint a grid of two-inch squares on your easel. When you project your negative, it helps you locate the area you want to make your tests on. That area should have the same average tonality as the picture's point of interest, with a contrast range fairly typical of the picture as a whole that you are exposing.

Now cut a sheet of enlarging paper into two-inch squares, and set one square down on the test area you selected.

exposing the test square

With the enlarger lens at its largest opening, expose the test square for about 10 seconds, or whatever exposure time you're used to. Now expose a second square for the same length of time, but this time close the lens down one stop. Continue this process, closing down the lens one stop each time you expose a new square, but keeping the enlarging time constant for each of the different exposures.

Now fan the test squares like a hand of cards, put them in your tongs, and process them together to ensure that all get equal development. After the stop bath you can carefully examine them in white light.

You probably won't find a single test square with just the right exposure, but one that's just a trifle light, and one just a trifle dark. Once you have determined this, use the f-stop that produced the lighter of the two almost-right exposures, make three more tests, increasing the exposure by one-fourth of the original time for each. In other words, if the right exposure was between 10 seconds at f/8 and 10 seconds at f/11, expose 13½, 15 and 17½ seconds at f/11. Total elapsed time for the series was 95 seconds; but conventional test-stripping, doubling exposure time instead of changing f-stops each time, would have taken 310 seconds.

The painted grid isn't an absolute necessity—it's just to help you lay each test square down on the same spot. Don't worry about its leaving a grid pattern reflected through the back of your prints—none of our prints show that problem.

Frame movies with a matte box

Here's a Hollywood-style
special-effects device that you can adapt
to almost any home-movie camera. It
gives your movies that professional look

BY JAMES R. OSWALD

■ USING SOME NEARBY OBJECTS to put a frame around your movie shots can make a good shot even better, by adding depth and atmosphere to a pretty scene that might otherwise look flat and dull on your screen. Look carefully, and you'll find suitable objects all around you—overhanging trees, picturesque archways, portholes, windows—the list is limited only by your imagination, by what the subject of your particular shot calls for, and by the location of these natural frames.

But often the right object to silhouette in your foreground isn't quite in the right place to frame your subject. And sometimes you may want to spice a shot with a frame not naturally on the scene—a keyhole, perhaps, or the overlapping circles of movie "binoculars" (real binoculars, of course, show more of a fuzzy oval than the sharp figure-8 pattern the movies show you).

Professional filmmakers always have the frames they need, though, whenever they need them. Their frames are small cutouts called "mattes," attached to their cameras with simple devices called "matte boxes." The effect is quite professional—but the construction of a matte box is so simple that you can easily build your own.

It's basically just a tapered, light-tight box painted black inside, with a round hole at its small end to admit the camera lens, and provision for mounting interchangeable framing masks over the other end. Dimensions vary from camera to camera. The small end of the box should be just large enough to admit the front of your lens.

The dimensions of the other end will depend upon the type of lens you have: With a zoom lens, you should be able to see the edges of any mask in your finder when the lens is set to its shortest focal length, yet be unable to see the mask when the lens is zoomed to its telephoto position. With a nonzoom lens, you want the edges of the mask to be visible when the mask is mounted, but for the edges of the mattebox to be out of the frame

Construction is simple, but dimensions must be adapted to each camera model

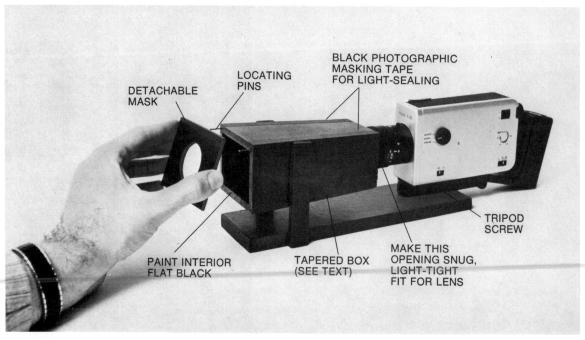

DETACHABLE MASK

LOCATING PINS

BLACK PHOTOGRAPHIC MASKING TAPE FOR LIGHT-SEALING

TRIPOD SCREW

PAINT INTERIOR FLAT BLACK

TAPERED BOX (SEE TEXT)

MAKE THIS OPENING SNUG, LIGHT-TIGHT FIT FOR LENS

The variety of mattes is unlimited. Other shapes could be cut from photos of trees, etc.

when the mask is off. The mask size also depends on the length of the box—and the length must be a compromise; the longer you make it, the more sharply outlined your matte frame will be—but the more ungainly and harder to handle the box will be, too.

Both the top and sides of the box should taper evenly and symmetrically, and the box's cross section should be a rectangle, approximately three quarters as high as it is wide.

With most cameras, the box will have to sit on struts above the baseboard, as mine does; again, the height of the struts depends on the camera. You can make your box from ¼-inch hardboard, plywood, opaque plastic, or what have you. Suit-

able scraps of wood can usually be picked up from lumberyards for a song. For the base, use ½-inch lumber. Drill the base below the tripod-screw socket, and let your tripod's screw hold both the camera and the matte box assembly.

The mattes themselves can be cut from ⅛-inch hardboard, wood, cardboard, or similar material. Four ¾-inch brads in the corners of the box's "window" end mate with small holes in the matte's corners to hold them in place.

To finish, tape the corners of the box with black photographic tape to prevent light leaks, and kill interior reflections by painting the inside of the box with flat black paint.

A few of the possible effects are shown above.

Exposure meters— use them right

BY IVAN BERGER

A dark face works here, but it's not always the effect you want

Exposed for the dark sweater, this shot washed out subject's face

A good exposure catches details in both the face and sweater

Light meters give different answers when you ask them different questions. A reflected-light meter at the camera position read both the backlit subject and the sky (left half of photo above), recommended an exposure that made the sky 18 percent gray but silhouetted the face. A close-up reading by the same meter turned the face 18 percent gray (right half of photo above), but washed out the sky

A meter reading taken from the subject's face gives maximum detail, but darkens the skin

Metering important details (here, the sweater) brings them out—but faces are often exceptions

Incident reading (with meter pointed at the camera) usually provides balanced results

■ EXPOSURE METERS—whether hand-held or built into your camera—can be awfully helpful, but they're also awfully dumb. They don't know what you're shooting, or how you want it shown. But with your brain guiding their electronic eyes, they can give you perfect—not just passable—results just about every time.

Even without your help, meters give good results in average picture-taking situations—which, by definition, means they'll give you good exposure most of the time. The brainwork comes in recognizing the non-average situation, and knowing how to deal with it.

Unassisted by your brain, a meter tells you just one thing: the exposure which will produce a negative whose tones all average out to middle gray from whatever subject is in the meter's field of view. If the subject *is* a middle gray—or a scene with an average mixture of equally important light or dark tones—that's just fine. But if the subject is predominantly dark or light, or much darker or lighter than its background, or if the meter picks up some of the light source that's illuminating the subject, the meter's accurate but unintelligent advice will lead you astray.

problems caused by backlighting

Backlight and contrasting backgrounds cause the most problems to amateur photographers. That's one reason you're so often told to face your subjects into the sun, even though it makes them squint and produces deep, harsh shadows. With the sun behind the subject, eyes would be comfortable and open, the face in soft shadow, and the hair glowing, perhaps, from the sun's rays. But a meter at the camera position (or built into the camera) would try to average this small, shadowed face with the vast bright sky behind it. Follow the meter blindly, and you wind up with a deep blue sky (gray, in black-and-white) and a dark, featureless facial blob.

Close-up metering is one answer to this problem. Move your meter in so it's reading just your subject, not its background, and that part of the problem's solved. This technique works equally well with hand-held meters, with meters built into nonautomatic cameras, and with those electric-eye automatic cameras whose meters can be locked into a particular reading by pressing the shutter button halfway down (which covers most such cameras we've tried).

But it doesn't work, of course, if there's some reason why you can't get in close to your subject, whether it's inaccessible or because it would make your subject self-conscious. If you're stand-

Close-up or spot metering solves some exposure problems

Close-up metering, whether done with a hand-held meter (top) or a camera's built-in one (above center), gives a reading for main details and avoids errors caused by contrasting backgrounds. Most electric-eye cameras, like this Konica, lock the meter readings when you press the shutter halfway; once the reading's right, you step back to shoot. A palm (bottom) can be used as a substitute for an inaccessible face

ing in the same light as your subject (as you usually are, in daylight) you can take a reading from a substitute subject of equal brightness— your hand, for example, if you're shooting a face. If the light is the same but no equally bright objects are handy, you can meter from a lighter or darker object, then adjust your exposure accordingly.

Professionals and some well-heeled amateurs buy spot meters like the Minolta and Honeywell Pentax models shown on page 175. These have meter-coverage angles of only 1° (though they show you a wider area, for easier aiming)—narrow enough to meter just a face at up to about 35 feet.

More compact and less expensive are the semi-spot meters like the Sekonic Zoom, or attachments like the Luna-Pro's which reduce meter coverage from its normal 30° to a somewhat narrower 7½° or 15°. The meters built into most single-lens reflex cameras are, in effect, semi-spot types, whether they read everything on the ground glass or just a selected area of it—but you can make them more selective by metering through a long telephoto lens.

But the world's not middle gray, which is why we said that close-up or spot metering only solves exposure problems part way. The exposure your meter recommends when reading your subject close-up will register that subject on the film as a middle gray—fine for deeply tanned faces, perhaps, but not for either dark or light ones—let alone for true tonal rendition of white or black objects.

compensating for light variations

To compensate, of course, you just give more or less exposure than the meter indicates, to lighten or darken the results. This is especially true for color slides, where you can't correct tonality as you can when printing from negatives. Fair skin, for instance, requires about one stop more exposure than indicated; white objects about two. In an otherwise sunlit scene, shaded subjects or tones about as dark as tree leaves require about one stop less exposure than the meter indicates; dark or deeply shadowed subjects in a sunlit scene require two stops less.

You can, of course, pick a typical middle tone in your scene as the subject for a spot or close-up

Aiming the meter down (left) means that the meter will read the subject, not the sky glare, especially on overcast days. But make sure the meter points at a representative subject tone, not much lighter or darker than the main subject. Meter cell types (below left) are easy to tell apart: Selenium cell (upper meter) has a big window, and selenium meters need no batteries. CdS cells (lower meter) have a smaller window, need batteries, but read in dimmer light. Of the meters shown just below, the four on the right are CdS types, as are all those in the bottom photo; the rest are selenium meters

Meters plain (above) and fancy (left) cover a wide range of shapes and prices. Plain units include: (1) Gossen Pilot, $40; (2) Weston Master VI with incident-light dome, $55; (3) Weston XM-1, $19; (4) Vivitar 34 clip-on, $19; (5) Weston XM-2, $34; (6) Vivitar 30, $14; (7) Sekonic Auto-Lumi L86, $17; (8) Vivitar 43, $27; (9) Gossen Super-Pilot, $75. Fancy Units are: (1) Minolta Auto Spot 1° meter, $340; (2) Sekonic L-228, 8.2°-28° zoom, $85; (3) Honeywell Pentax, 1°/21° spot, $205; (4) Sekonic studio deluxe incident meter, $65; (5) Gossen Luna-Pro, $125 and $35, 7½°/ 15° spot attachment; (6) Minolta Autometer professional, $110, and its $30, 10° spot attachment

Clip-on meters can also be hand-held; the $87 Leicameter (left) couples to
M-model Leicas. The $19 Vivitar 24 fits any camera with an accessory shoe

reading, and get accurate results that way. Or you can meter the darkest and lightest of the important subject areas (those in which you're trying to hold detail), and set your camera for an exposure halfway between the meter's two recommendations.

Low-contrast scenes, such as those made on overcast days or in mist or fog, tend to look overexposed even when they aren't, because the blacks register unnaturally light. Try exposing one stop less than the meter's recommendation. But if you're trying for pastel tones in color shots, try giving one stop *more* exposure than indicated.

Measure incident light, though, and you can avoid the need for most of these compensations. Incident light is the light falling on the subject, not the light reflected from it; incident meters tell you what exposure will give you a middle-gray photo from a middle-gray subject under whatever light's at hand. Lighter and darker subjects will register this automatically.

A few meters, like the Sekonic Studio and Minolta Auto-Professional on page 175, are basically designed for incident-light use; many reflected-light meters also have translucent white incident adapters that snap onto or slide over their light cells.

Usually, incident meters are held at the subject position and pointed at the camera. That's one reason why incident meters are so rarely used: It's a nuisance to walk back and forth to measure, and impractical to build such meters into cameras, (though some camera meters can be adapted).

Of course, if the illumination at the camera position is the same as the light falling on the subject, you can take a reading right where you are; just be sure the meter still has its back to the subject. This makes incident meters as handy as spot-meters under many outdoor conditions.

Since incident meters basically figure the exposure that an 18 percent-reflective middle gray object would require, any reflected-light meter can give incident readings if it's aimed at an 18 percent gray card, (available from many photo stores).

You needn't even use a gray card—any object of known reflectance will do just as well, provided you change your exposure to compensate. If you use your hand, for instance, give your shots one stop more exposure than the meter indicates. If you use a white card (a very handy metering trick in dim light, where a meter may be unable to read clearly), give two stops more.

Creative judgment comes into play when the "correct" exposure you get by aiming the meter properly and interpreting the results isn't the right exposure for the artistic effect you're aiming at. Where incident light meters tell you how to avoid silhouetting your subject in a backlit shot, for instance, you might *want* a silhouette effect, in which case you'd have to underexpose considerably to get what you're after. If you're trying for a light, "high-key" effect, you'll want to give your photo more exposure than the meter recommends; for dark, "low-key" effects, you'll want to give it less exposure.

Such creative disobedience to the meter's suggestions are worth learning—but only once you've learned what those suggestions really mean.

How to solder wiring

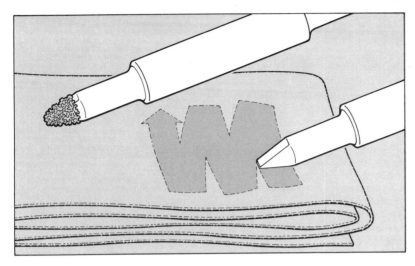

Keep your iron clean

A dirty iron won't transfer its heat to the joint efficiently. For best results, "tin" your iron's tip with a thin, shiny coating of solder before using it. After every few joints, clean the tip with a damp cloth or sponge—more often, if it acquires a dirty, dark or charred look, like the one shown at the far left. After cleaning, if the tip has lost its shiny appearance, re-tin it with another thin coat of solder. When the job is finished, clean and re-tin your iron again before you put it away

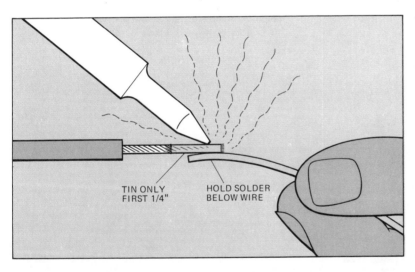

TIN ONLY FIRST 1/4"

HOLD SOLDER BELOW WIRE

Tin wires carefully

Tinning any wire with a thin coat of solder makes it easier to solder to a joint. Tinning stranded wires also helps hold the strands together at the tip. Hold the solder below the wire so it will soak in, not drip on, and remove it and the iron once the solder has soaked into the first ¼ inch of the wire. Don't tin the remaining wire—it could become brittle and the joint break if wires are flexed or pulled. When soldering shielded cable, be careful not to melt the insulation by applying too much heat

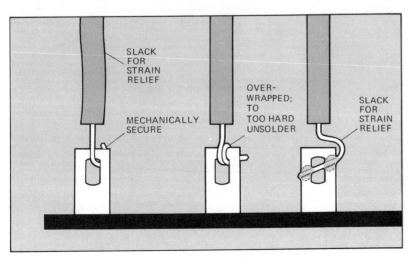

SLACK FOR STRAIN RELIEF

MECHANICALLY SECURE

OVER-WRAPPED; TO TOO HARD UNSOLDER

SLACK FOR STRAIN RELIEF

Make solid connections

Before soldering, wires should be bent to form mechanically secure connections (far left) that can stay in place even without solder; the solder's job is to maintain good electrical contact, not to glue wires in place. Leave some slack in the wire too, to prevent strain on the connection. Too complex a wrap (center) makes it harder to unsolder the wire for servicing. But a solder-only connection, with no wrapping, will usually yield a "cold-solder" joint

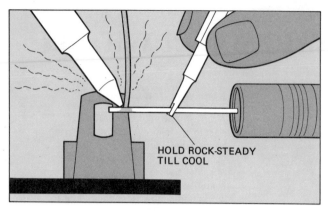

Keep wires stationary while cooling

Wires that move while the solder cools cause unreliable "cold-solder" joints. If you can't hold the wires in place with a good mechanical connection (as shown above, where a component lead is too short), hold them in place with soldering aids or other tools until the joint is cool. Brace your hands if necessary, to prevent shaking. Don't try to hold wires in place with the soldering iron—they'll spring up again as soon as you take the iron away. Soldering aids, of metal that solder doesn't stick to, also have many other uses

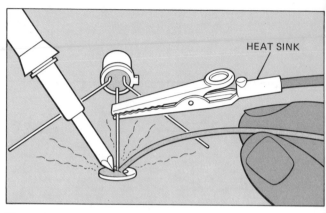

Heat sinks protect transistors

The heat of soldering can cook transistors and integrated circuits. If you're not using sockets, clip a heat sink between the joint and the transistor body to prevent this. Commercially made heat sinks are good, but you can also make your own from an alligator clip with a stub of heavy copper wire attached; or cement some felt into the clip's jaws and moisten it before each use. With no heat sink, use the least-powerful iron that will bring the joint quickly to soldering temperature. Too-small irons will cook more transistors than you'd think

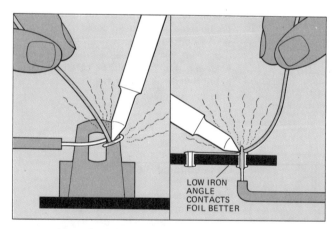

Heat the joint first, then solder

Don't just melt the solder and drip it onto the joint. First, heat the joint with the iron for a few seconds, then move the solder into contact with both the iron tip and all the parts or wires to be soldered. When the joint is hot enough, the solder will flow over and into it, wetting it evenly, filling in spaces, and cooling to a smooth, silvery sheen. If the joint takes more than three or four seconds to heat, though, you're using too small an iron for that job

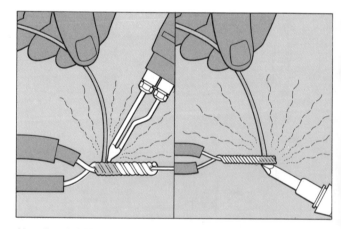

Use the right iron for the job

Electronic soldering is usually done best with medium-wattage pencil irons—hot enough to heat fine electronic wires quickly without cooking components. Heavy household wiring jobs are best done with high-wattage guns, powerful enough to heat the joint rapidly without having to bake wires and insulation for minutes; guns, which cool off between joints, are also handier than continuous-heating irons in the awkward places typical of house-wiring and other electrical situations

How to tell good solder joints from bad ones

Good solder joints (A) are smooth and shiny, with the outlines of all wires and contacts clearly visible, but with rounded fillets of solder filling in the gaps and corners where wires meet. Insufficient solder (B) leaves no fillets and may not maintain a reliable connection. Too much solder (C) covers a connection with big blobs (which sometimes cause short-circuit bridges between conductors on circuit boards); there may be a good joint underneath, but you can't see it to tell. Overheating (D) chars wire insulation and may lift solder pads from circuit boards or harm delicate components. Cold solder joints may have a jagged, crystalline look (E), a dripped-on, blobby appearance not conformant to outlines of the joint (F), or merely a hazy, milky sheen (not shown)

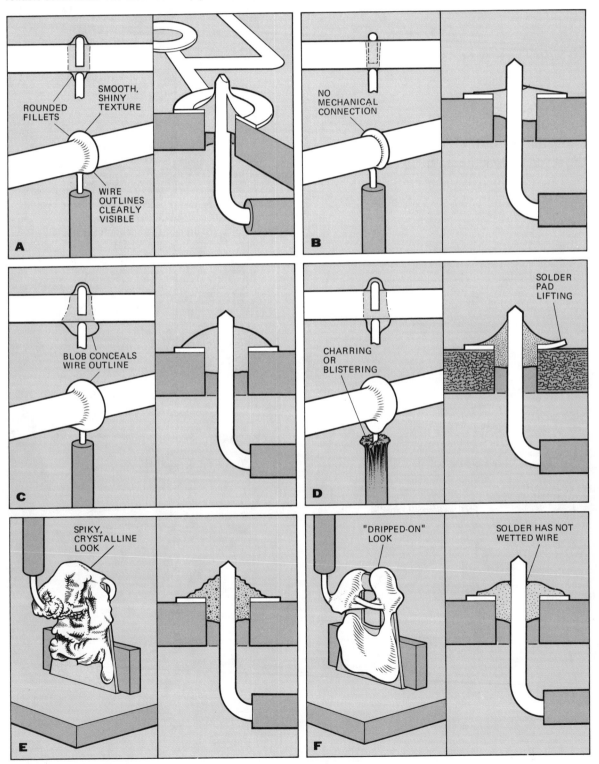

A
ROUNDED FILLETS
SMOOTH, SHINY TEXTURE
WIRE OUTLINES CLEARLY VISIBLE

B
NO MECHANICAL CONNECTION

C
BLOB CONCEALS WIRE OUTLINE

D
CHARRING OR BLISTERING
SOLDER PAD LIFTING

E
SPIKY, CRYSTALLINE LOOK

F
"DRIPPED-ON" LOOK
SOLDER HAS NOT WETTED WIRE

A game to test your cool

BY KENNETH WELLS

You need nerves as hard
as the steel balls in this
interesting but frustrating game to get
the seven balls in the seven holes

Prick punch (below) is used to transfer the template holes to the hardwood center and base members. The ⅜-in. holes are drilled (bottom photo) at points A first, then 1⅛-in. holes at points B

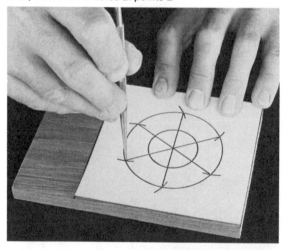

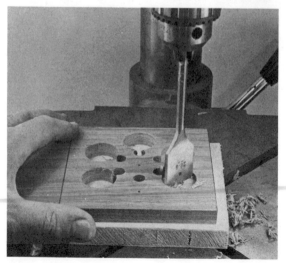

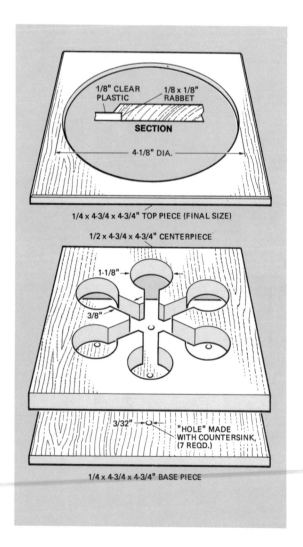

1/8" CLEAR PLASTIC   1/8 x 1/8" RABBET

SECTION

4-1/8" DIA.

1/4 x 4-3/4 x 4-3/4" TOP PIECE (FINAL SIZE)

1/2 x 4-3/4 x 4-3/4" CENTERPIECE

1-1/8"

3/8"

3/32" "HOLE" MADE WITH COUNTERSINK, (7 REQD.)

1/4 x 4-3/4 x 4-3/4" BASE PIECE

PATIENCE IS THE NAME of the game and that's what it takes, plus a steady hand, to work this fascinating and sometimes frustrating game of skill. The object: Make seven steel balls come to rest in seven individual holes, but it isn't easy. Chances are, you'll give up more times than not.

To produce several for gifts or for sale, it will pay you to make a cardboard template to aid in quickly prick-punching the 13 holes to be drilled in the center member and the seven $\frac{3}{32}$-in. V-holes in the base which are made with a countersink.

The five work photos take you through the important steps in making the game. The maple center and base members are cut 4¾-in. square, but the top member is cut oversize initially and then to its final size after a 3⅛-in. hole and rabbet are turned in it for a round ⅛-in.-thick Plexiglas window. You can use double-back, pressure-sensitive tape or small screws in the waste to mount the work (bottom side out) to a faceplate block.

Template holes A and B are used for marking the center member, holes A being made with a ⅜-in. twist bit, holes B with a 1⅛-in. spade bit. Template holes A are also used to mark the location of the seven V-holes in the base member. Sand the top of the base member smooth before gluing it to the center member, then apply two coats of white shellac and rub with fine steel wool. If you can't find the ⁵⁄₁₆-in. steel balls locally, write Way-Mar Co., Box 164, Hartsdale, N.Y. 10530.

Paring the passageways between the 1⅛-in. holes is done with a sharp chisel guided by a straightedge. The seven V-holes in base are made with tip of a countersink (bottom), each hole being only 3/32-in.

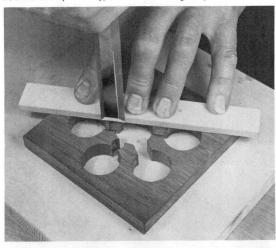

template for hole centers

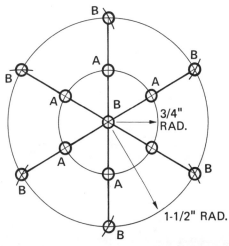

Circular opening and rabbet in top member are turned by mounting work on a flat block fastened to faceplate

181

Go build a kite

Make one of these fancy fliers—
from a kit or from scratch—to take
advantage of any brisk wind

BY STEPHEN WALTON

■ SOME GREAT KITES come in kit form these days. The pyramid-shaped Tetra and the versatile Skylinks, shown in its catamaran-like, stunt-kite configuration, are easy to assemble from plastic components. The Red Baron at center, patterned after a World War I Fokker Triplane, is a different story—all its parts except plastic wing roots must be cut to shape, taking about 14 hours. At the

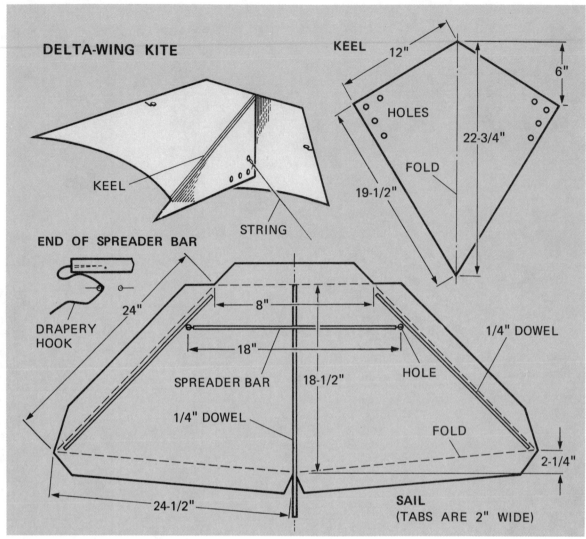

DELTA-WING KITE

KEEL

12"

6"

HOLES

22-3/4"

FOLD

19-1/2"

KEEL

STRING

END OF SPREADER BAR

24"

**DRAPERY
HOOK**

8"

1/4" DOWEL

18"

HOLE

SPREADER BAR

18-1/2"

1/4" DOWEL

FOLD

2-1/4"

24-1/2"

SAIL
(TABS ARE 2" WIDE)

The frame parts—wing spars, spine and spreader bar—of the delta-wing kite are all ½-in.
dowel. Material for the sail and keel is ½-mil metallized Mylar

build a kite, continued

lower left is a scratch-built delta kite in metallized Mylar—but you could make an equally airworthy version using nothing more than polyethylene trash bags for sail material.

The TetraKite, by Synestructics, Inc., takes its name from its tetrahedral shape, the shape favored by Alexander Graham Bell (the same one who invented the telephone) during his kite research. Since tetrahedrons pack together just as neatly in space as equilateral triangles do on a plane surface, a tetrahedral kite can have as many cells or lifting units as desired, each a tetrahedron with two sides covered with sail material—Bell built one with 3393 cells that was able to lift a man. A SuperTetraKite that's made up of four

TetraKites is also available; 5½ ft. on an edge, it's too big to fit through most doors, and so requires final assembly outdoors.

From the same manufacturer, Skylinks is a kite system based on triangular box-kite modules. These can be flown separately or in train, or assembled into larger kites like the one shown on page 182, a kite designed for dual-line stunt flying.

The Red Baron is one of four airplane-style kite kits manufactured by Straton Air Engineering. It flies with a high angle of attack, its wings acting as sails, not airfoils. The dihedral angle of the wing-sails gives stability. In principle, it's not too dissimilar to three of the tetrahedral cells that make up the TetraKite stacked one on top of the other.

We ran several flight tests with the kites, but the flying weather available was generally gusty. Join the fun yourself, and see how these kites perform on days when the wind is steady or relatively calm.

Hard landings (resulting from the attempt to fly in unreliable wind) broke a couple of the TetraKite's spars. On a day with very little wind, the Red Baron proved itself a stable flyer. Its apparent fragility was no drawback, since—in a steady breeze—it was easy to fly to soft landings, both on the ground and to the hand.

how to build the delta-wing

The delta-wing kite is easy to build. Make a full-size pattern on newspaper or wrapping paper from the pattern shown on the preceding page. Obtain ½-mil Mylar and cut it to size with a razor blade. This will give the smoothest possible edge and avoid tearing. Fold the mainsail tabs over and glue them down with rubber cement. Attach the wing spars and the spine to the sail using rubber cement and strapping tape to fasten them in place.

Fold the keel into a single triangle, closing its open sides with strapping tape. Attach the keel to the under side of the sail with a strip of strapping tape along either side of the long edge. Holes for the spreader bar and the bridling holes get double patches of tape—with grain perpendicular—on either side of the Mylar, and eyelets for further protection against rips. Putting more than one bridling hole in the keel will allow you to make adjustments for the best flying characteristics after experimentation. The spreader bar has drapery hooks set into dowel ends; pointed end hooks can be hammered in without splitting the dowel, but they should be secured with a dab of epoxy to be sure they won't come out during flight.

If you are making the kite with polyethylene,

use cellophane tape instead of strapping tape. The rubber cement is unnecessary—just hold the tabs down with tape. Also omit the folded-up tab on the main sail's trailing edge.

how to fly the kites

Normally it shouldn't be necessary to run with a kite to get it into the air. In brisk winds, most kites will take off directly from your hand. If you don't have any luck with this type of launch, there are two other possible ways for you to go. One is to set the kite on the ground as close as possible to its flying position. (Watch out for obstacles that it may get snared on). Then back off from the kite about 100 ft. When you feel a puff of wind, tug on the string to lift the kite off the ground. Then start hauling in the line as rapidly as possible to give the kite the desired altitude. The other alternative to a hand launch requires an assistant. He should position himself with the kite about 100 ft. downwind from you. Have him toss the kite into the air when he feels the wind coming up. This should be done gently. You then haul in the line until the kite finds a steady breeze aloft and starts to pull on the line. A faltering kite can often be made to resume climbing by tugging once or twice on the line; hauling in line is the more drastic way to get a sinking kite back up. Quite often the windspeed will be higher as the kite ascends. This means that even though you have trouble getting the kite launched, you still may have a successful flight if you can get the kite high enough to catch these stronger winds.

Part of the skill involved in kiteflying is getting a kite to go higher and farther under less than ideal conditions. This is a knack you acquire through experimentation and practice. It also helps to use equipment which gives you maximum control over the motions of your kite as it ascends with the wind.

use a rod and reel for control

This means using a rod and reel to fly your kite. A good baitcasting reel works well for this. Your thumb on the spool acts as a natural brake, letting you feed line at the proper rate to a pulling kite. A rod not only gives you a place to mount the reel, making it easier for you to use, but provides increased leverage for line movement. Don't use a full-length rod, of course, just the bottom part of a sectional rod or a telescoping rod in the closed position.

You'll find that a rod also gives you much more control for bringing the kite down and will help you achieve soft landings.

Fun with a chain saw

Make a hippo with a chain saw? Sure! It's quite a challenge to
use a chain saw to express yourself creatively

■ MOST HOMEOWNERS think of a chain saw as a one-purpose tool intended for cutting logs. But it's more than that: Carpenters, journeymen and wood sculptors have long known a chain saw can be put to good use on chores from rough carpentry to carving. The projects shown on the facing page are in these areas. The patio furniture, with its rough-hewn look, is whittled from logs in less time than you'd imagine. Planter, totem pole and the yard toy are fun to make and offer a real challenge to satisfy your creature urges, as well as develop a new skill.

First, build a sturdy sawbuck; it's an indispensable aid in chain-saw cutting. In this version, carriage bolts—instead of nails—are used to fasten the legs. When not needed, the buck can be closed flat and stored against a wall.

Important points to keep in mind when constructing your buck: The Xs should be joined at a distance about 12 to 14 in. from the top of the legs, and the angle between legs at top should be about 70 to 75°. In any event, it should not exceed 90°.

Some chain-saw know-how. As with all power tools, if basic safety rules are followed, the chain saw is a safe tool to work with. Before you use your saw, take time to read the manufacturer's manual, including the section on safety practices. To rip a log—for the tabletop, for example—place it on two or more supports. Make certain the log is held firmly with nails or cradles at the ends to keep it from rolling. For precision ripping, use a guide board to support the saw's weight as you cut.

All projects shown, except the table, are cut from single logs. Overall dimensions to suit your patio size can be used to determine the table size. The tabletop is held together by a pair of 2x4s nailed to its underside; two 5-ft. logs are split and nailed together to form the X legs. Legs are secured to the tabletop with nails after notching the appropriate logs where they meet the 2x4s. The only critical dimension for chair and stool is the seat height (for comfort). Floor to seat-top measurement should be about 16 in.

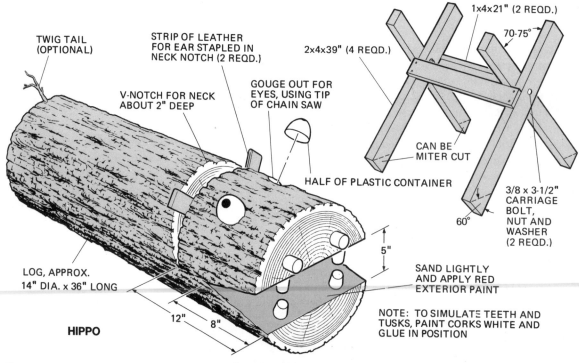

TWIG TAIL
(OPTIONAL)

STRIP OF LEATHER
FOR EAR STAPLED IN
NECK NOTCH (2 REQD.)

V-NOTCH FOR NECK
ABOUT 2" DEEP

GOUGE OUT FOR
EYES, USING TIP
OF CHAIN SAW

LOG, APPROX.
14" DIA. x 36" LONG

HALF OF PLASTIC CONTAINER

12"   8"

HIPPO

1x4x21" (2 REQD.)

70-75°

2x4x39" (4 REQD.)

CAN BE
MITER CUT

3/8 x 3-1/2"
CARRIAGE
BOLT,
NUT AND
WASHER
(2 REQD.)

60°

5"

SAND LIGHTLY
AND APPLY RED
EXTERIOR PAINT

NOTE: TO SIMULATE TEETH AND
TUSKS, PAINT CORKS WHITE AND
GLUE IN POSITION

Not all felled trees wind up in the fireplace. Log projects in photo at left, viewed clockwise from hippo are: three-legged stool, totem pole, picnic table, planter and four-legged chair. Projects were created using a 14-in. chain saw. Table requires a hammer and nails

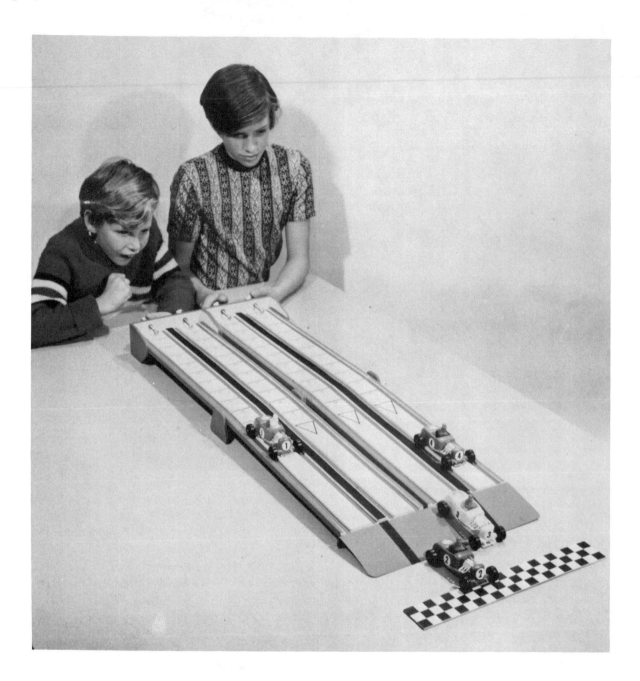

Toy racetrack

By NELLO J. ORSINI

■ HERE'S AN EXCITING toy that will provide youngsters with all the thrills of a real speedway. I call it the Derby Hill 500. Four plastic cars are sent roaring down the track by two or four "drivers," each pulling one or two spring plungers. The car that goes the farthest or crosses the checkered finish line first wins.

Stovebolt slipped through coil spring and capped with drawer knob makes a plunger to propel the cars. Holes for plungers are centered in each track lane

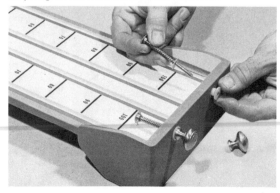

The four roadbed sections required can be placed either side by side or end to end to vary the fun. Placed in pairs side by side, the sections provide a four-track raceway 36-in. long. Hooked end to end, the sections provide a 6-ft.-long raceway. In the latter case, only two cars are driven and drivers are stationed at opposite ends, each taking turns racing his car down and up the inclined track. The driver who scores a total of 500 points first wins.

Each roadbed section measures 7-in. wide by 18-in. long and has four ½-in.-wide grooves spaced to suit the wheels of the particular plastic race cars used. The cars I used were purchased at Woolworth's and are about 6-in. long.

The drawings show how the roadbed sections are supported and how they hook together. Metal angles formed from sheet aluminum engage saw kerfs in the support blocks. The outboard end of the track hooks similarly into an open fold in the metal ramp.

Stick-on scoring numerals are used for marking the track, and ⅛-in. black matte charting tape (Prestype) is used to rule off scoring divisions.

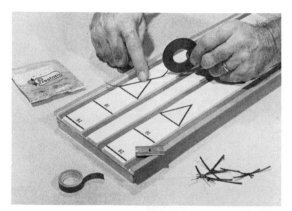

Black charting tape, ⅛-in. wide, is used to rule lines on track surface (top). Green tape marks wheel channels; press-on numerals make neat numbering job

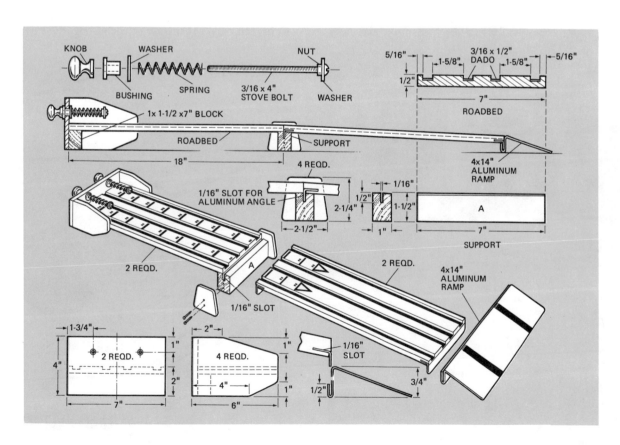

Bean-bag bull's-eye

BY CAROLYN FARRELL

Opponents stand at each side of platform and take turns throwing two bean bags in succession at the bull's-eye. Platforms are spaced about 10 ft. apart for youngsters

BULL'S EYE IS a game that can be played rain or shine, indoors and out, by youngsters and oldsters alike. In some ways it is played like horse-shoes. The difference is that you use bean-bags and try to make a "ringer" by tossing a bag right into a hole.

The rules are very simple. A hole-in-one scores three points; a bag that lands and stays on top of the platform, one point. In case a skilled opponent scores two bull's-eyes in succession, his score of six points wipes out an earlier four-point score of his opponent. This then gives him a leading score of two. Each player throws two bags in succession, and the first to reach 21 points wins the game. From our experience it is best to place the platforms about 30 ft. apart for adults. When the kids begin playing, move them in to about 10 ft. apart to make it a little bit easier.

As you can probably imagine, there are many variations in scoring. One variation is when the game is played by adults who use eight bean-bags, four for each player. If either of the players should be skillful enough to toss all four bags in the bull's-eye in one turn, that player automatically wins the game.

The drawing below shows how the platforms are made. The top of each is made with ¼-in. hardboard and a 6-inch hole is cut with your sabre saw or jigsaw. This is then screwed to the pine base, which is cut to put the game on an angle towards the player throwing the bean-bag.

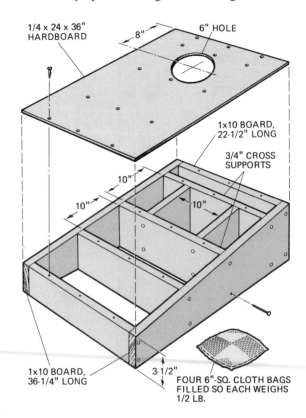

1/4 x 24 x 36" HARDBOARD — 8" — 6" HOLE

1x10 BOARD, 22-1/2" LONG

3/4" CROSS SUPPORTS

10" 10" 10"

1x10 BOARD, 36-1/4" LONG

3-1/2"

FOUR 6"-SQ. CLOTH BAGS FILLED SO EACH WEIGHS 1/2 LB.

Index

The page number refers to the first page on which specific information can be found.